THE SECRET LIFE OF PETS 2: ANNUAL 2020
A CENTUM BOOK 978-1-913072-30-8
Published in Great Britain by Centum Books Ltd
This edition published 2019
1 3 5 7 9 10 8 6 4 2

Centum Books Ltd, 20 Devon Square, Newton Abbot, Devon, TQ12 2HR, UK

books@centumbooksltd.co.uk

CENTUM BOOKS Limited Reg. No. 07641486

A CIP catalogue record for this book is available from the British Library.

Printed in China.

ILLUMINATION PRESENTS

THE SECRET LIFE OF PETS 2

THIS BOOK BELONGS TO:

....

CONTENTS

WELCOME TO THE SECRET LIFE OF PETS 2!

Max, Gidget, Snowball and all the Pets are ready for action. There are puzzles on Uncle Shep's farm, cat games galore – and a white tiger to be rescued! **The owners are away, so turn the page to find out what secrets are in store...**

WHAT MISSING SOCKS?

Pickles from Pops' Puppy School has got his paws on **9** odd socks. **Can you find them hidden on pages throughout the book?** Tick them below as you find them.

ANSWERS ON PAGE 75

MEET THE PETS!

Get to know the old gang and some new friends on the block.

MAX

Max lives the most pampered life imaginable. He's got a supportive brother in Duke, a loving owner in Katie and two new members of the family – Katie's husband, Chuck, and their baby boy Liam. Once wary of children, Max has come to adore Liam, following him around like a helicopter parent to make sure he is 100% safe at all times.

DUKE

Duke is Max's adopted brother and the enthusiastic answer to the question, "Who's a good boy?" He enjoys farm life and takes a far more relaxed approach towards the care of Liam, but he is always there for Max in his time of need.

GIDGET

Gidget is a well-groomed but gutsy pomeranian. When she accidentally knocks Max's favourite toy off the balcony into a cat lady's apartment, she has to learn from Chloe how to become a cat in order to infiltrate the cats' lair and get it back.

BUDDY

Buddy is a wiry, sarcastic dachshund who is part of Max's security team for Liam, watching the toddler's every move. He'll also suit up with Snowball to help rescue Hu, the tiger.

MEL

Mel is an excitable pug who struggles to stay focused when he's recruited by Max to be part of Liam's security detail. Even when he's supposed to be helping Snowball save Hu, he's got his own ulterior mission: *snacks.*

NORMAN

Norman the guinea pig is the most enthusiastic of the security team Max puts together to guard Liam. Unfortunately, Norman is the last Pet who should be in charge of any kind of 'intelligence'.

MEET THE PETS!

CHLOE

Chloe is a tabby cat with a passion for cake. She loves food, lying down and herself. Chloe lives above Max so she likes to visit him and, despite having a no-can-do attitude, she is always there for her friends.

SWEET PEA

This fearless budgie agrees to help Gidget learn the ways of the cat.

POPS

Pops is an old basset hound who tells it like it is. He has started a Puppy School, training pups to use their cuteness to get their own way.

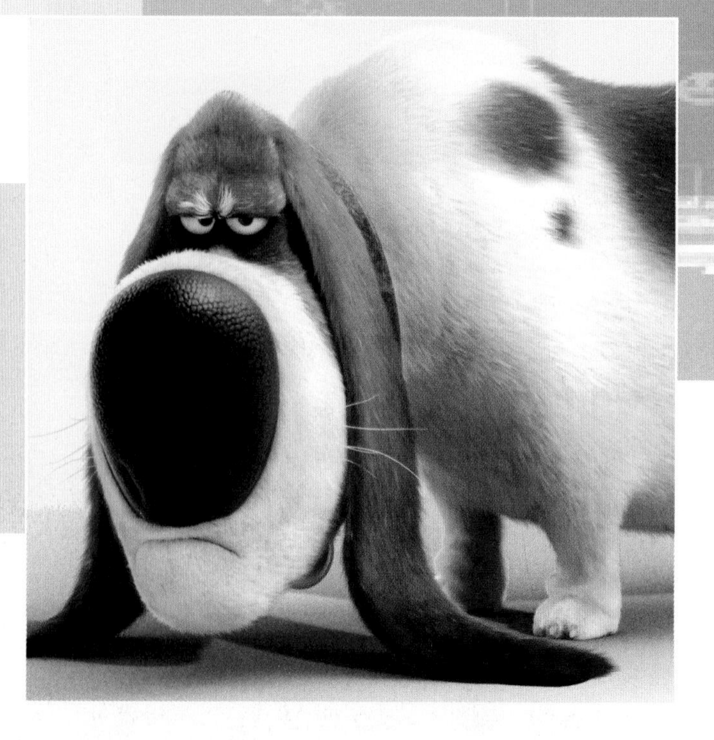

DAISY

Daisy is an adorable shih tzu with an enormous personality who isn't afraid to speak her mind. She and her new friend Snowball band together to save Hu.

SNOWBALL

Snowball is a former leader of an animal gang, and now an official domesticated Pet. He likes to watch super hero TV shows with his owner, Molly. Molly has made him a super hero costume and he likes to spend his day practising super hero stuff.

ROOSTER

Rooster is Max's new friend – a farm dog full of country knowledge. He wears a bandana and saves Max from a turkey with just one bark. Maybe this confident dog can teach Max to be calm and not worry so much.

COLOUR DAISY AND ROOSTER AND HIS BANDANA!

SPOT THE DIFFERENCE

The Pets are doing one of their favourite things – chasing butterflies around Central Park. **Can you spot six changes in the second picture of Mel?**

1

2

Who are your three favourite Pets?

1 ____________

2 ____________

3 ____________

ANSWERS ON PAGE 75

CITY MAZE

Max is really, really excited about going for a walk with Katie... until he realises it's a trip to the vet! **Can you work out what route they took through New York?**

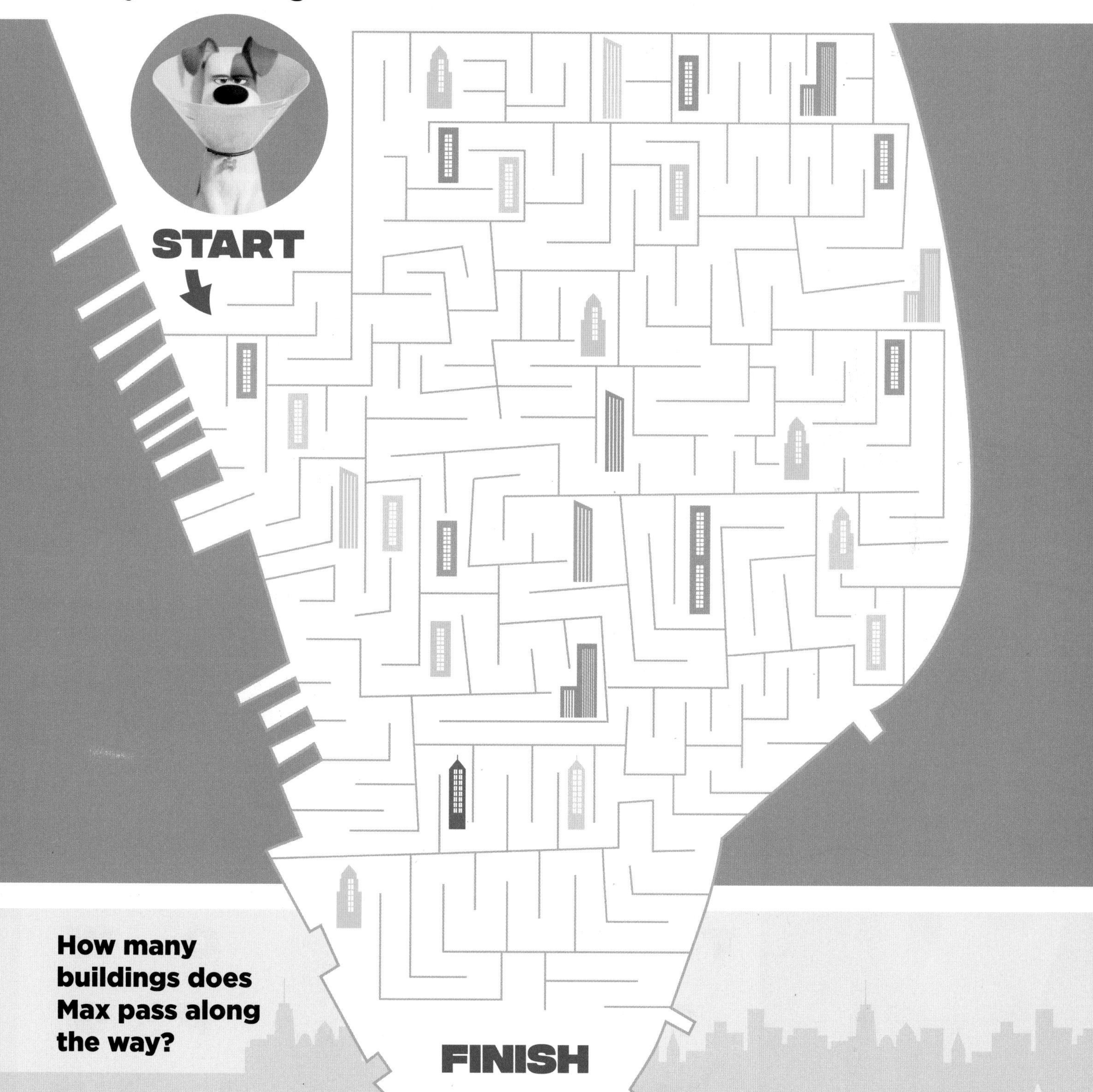

How many buildings does Max pass along the way?

ANSWER ON PAGE 75

FARM FRIGHTS!

Max is taken on a trip to Uncle Shep's farm, but this city dog doesn't know anything about country life! **Can you help him with these farmyard challenges?**

TURKEY RUN

Max is terrified of the turkey – especially when it's chasing after him! **Which line will help him avoid the fence and get safely into the field?**

A

B

C

Fill in the missing letters to reveal some things Max sees on the farm.

Use these letters in the empty spaces:

A E I O

TR__CT__R

C__W

F__NC__

P__G

WH__ __T

L__MB

ANSWERS ON PAGE 75

ALL MIXED UP

Max's time on the farm is a wild new venture. **Draw lines to match Max's farmyard expressions!**

COUNTING COWS

The farm is full of strange new animals that Max has never seen in the city. **Count the cows.**

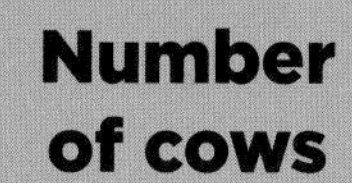

Number of cows

ANSWERS ON PAGE 75

GIDGET GAMES

While Max is on the farm, Gidget is at home with the other Pets having some **fun** of her own...

Who else is back at the apartment building with Gidget? **Match the Pets to the mystery shadows.**

Max leaves something precious behind with Gidget. **WHAT IS IT? Circle every third letter.**

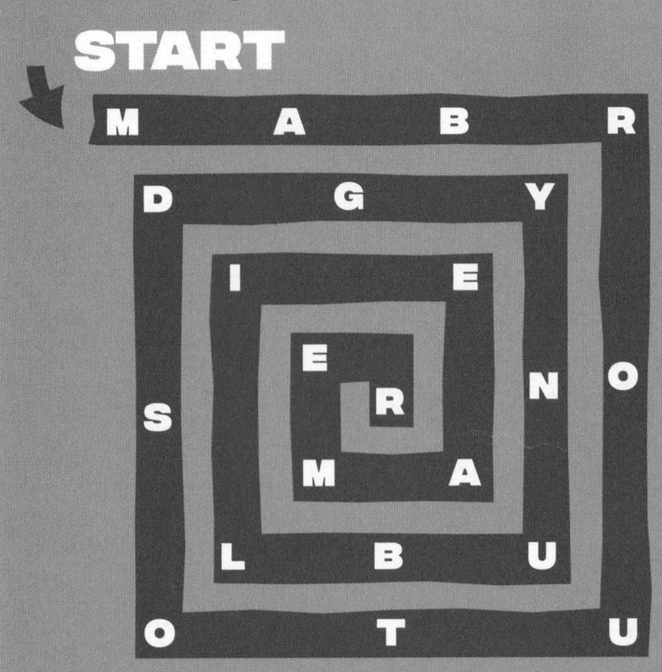

Write your answer here:

_____ _____ _____ _____

_____ _____ _____

ANSWERS ON PAGE 75

GIDGET LOVES...

Gidget is spoiled by her loving owners. **What three things would she choose from these items?**

ANSWER ON PAGE 75

PLAYTIME PUPS

Find a friend to play this game! Sit opposite each other with the puzzle pages and questions in front of you.

Count down to begin and see who gets the most Puppy School points!

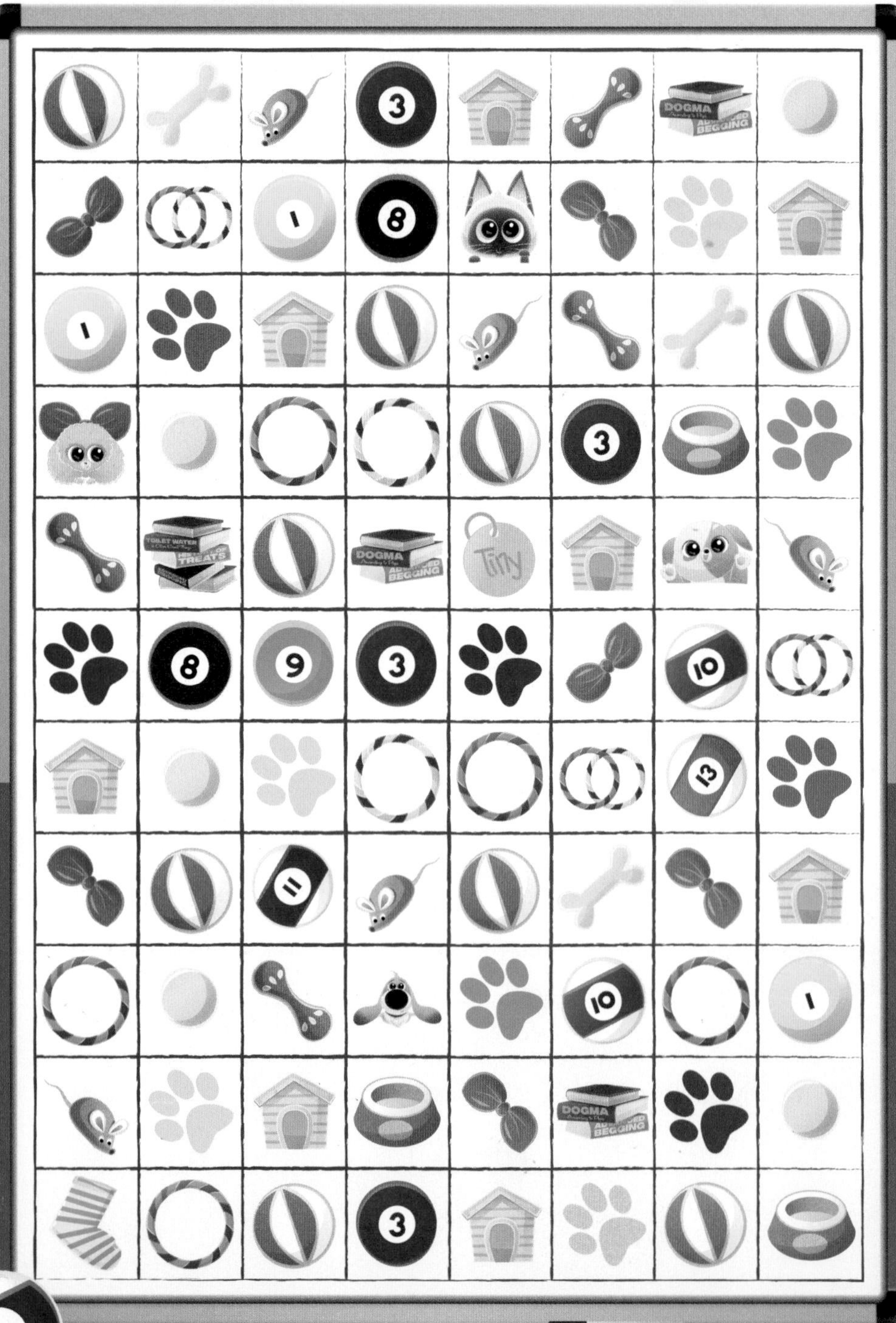

1. How many **bows** can you count in the grid?

☐

2. How many **paw prints** are there?

☐

3. Is there a number **9** pool ball?

☐

4. Can you circle three pups – **Princess, Pickles** and **Tiny** – in the grid?

☐

ANSWERS ON PAGE 75

How to add up your score:

- 1 point for the player who finishes first.
- 1 point for each correct answer.
- 1 point if you spot all three pups.

1. How many **bows** can you count in the grid?

2. How many **paw prints** are there?

3. Is there a number **9** pool ball?

4. Can you circle three pups – **Princess**, **Pickles** and **Tiny** – in the grid?

SNOWBALL'S SEARCH
HELP SNOWBALL SAVE HU BY FINDING THE WORDS BELOW. CAN YOU FIND ALL THESE WORDS HIDDEN IN THE GRID? LOOK UP, DOWN, ACROSS AND DIAGONALLY.
MOLLY
SUPER HERO
COSTUME
HU
TIGER
CIRCUS
SERGEI
SNOWBALL'S NEW FRIEND IS HIDING IN THE GRID, TOO. CAN YOU FIND HER?
ANSWERS ON PAGE 75

DESIGN A COSTUME

SNOWBALL'S AMAZING SUPER HERO COSTUME TRANSFORMS HIM INTO... CAPTAIN SNOWBALL! DESIGN YOUR OWN COSTUME FOR SNOWBALL IN ANY STYLE.

COSTUME STYLE: ____________________

SPECIAL FEATURES: ____________________

SNOWBALL'S NEW NICKNAME: ____________________

PET SCRAMBLES

The Pets are all running around the city on separate missions and they can't find each other. **Unscramble the names to get them back together – QUICK!**

G E T D I G

___ ___ ___ ___ ___ ___

U B D Y D

___ ___ ___ ___ ___

L A W B L O N S

___ ___ ___ ___ ___ ___ ___ ___

A X M

___ ___ ___

Y A I S D

___ ___ ___ ___ ___

K U D E

___ ___ ___ ___

E L O C H

___ ___ ___ ___ ___

ANSWERS ON PAGE 75

MAX'S CODE

Max is worried and sends out a message to all the Pets with his walkie-talkie system. **What is the message? Crack the code to find out.**

A	B	C	D	E	F	G	H	I	J	K	L	M
1	2	3	4	5	6	7	8	9	10	11	12	13

N	O	P	Q	R	S	T	U	V	W	X	Y	Z
14	15	16	17	18	19	20	21	22	23	24	25	26

2 1 2 25

12 9 1 13

9 19

13 9 19 19 9 14 7!

Colour Max once you have solved the code.

YOU CAN USE THE SAME CODE TO **SEND A SECRET MESSAGE TO A FRIEND!**

ANSWER ON PAGE 75

POPS' PUPPY SCHOOL

The puppy Pets are learning to get away with anything – just by using their extreme levels of cuteness! **Help them with their lessons in Puppy School.**

Practise being as adorable as Pickles!
Copy this picture of him so he's ready for his lessons. You can use the grid lines as a guide.

Who else is in class with Pickles?
Complete the names.

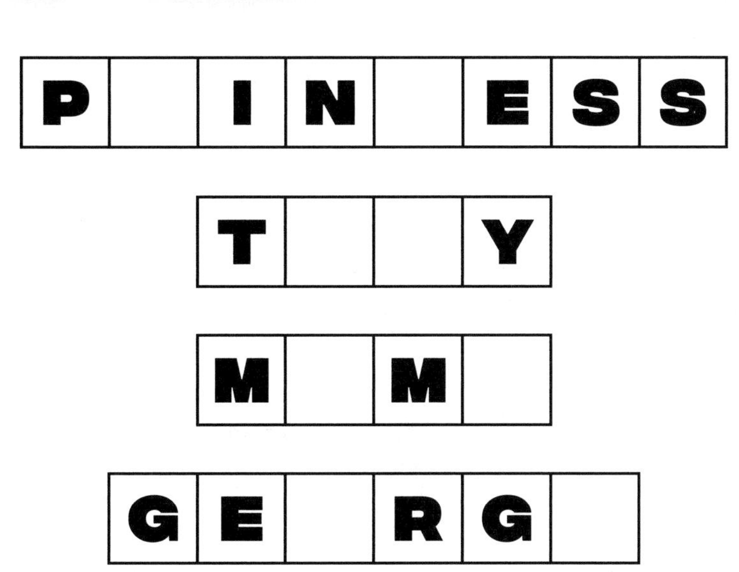

George attends Puppy School even though he's a kitten! ***Can you find his toy mouse?*** *It's a little different from all the others.*

ANSWERS ON PAGE 75

MIXED-UP MAX!

Uncle Shep's farm has Max all in a jumble! **Match the pieces to complete this jigsaw of Max.**

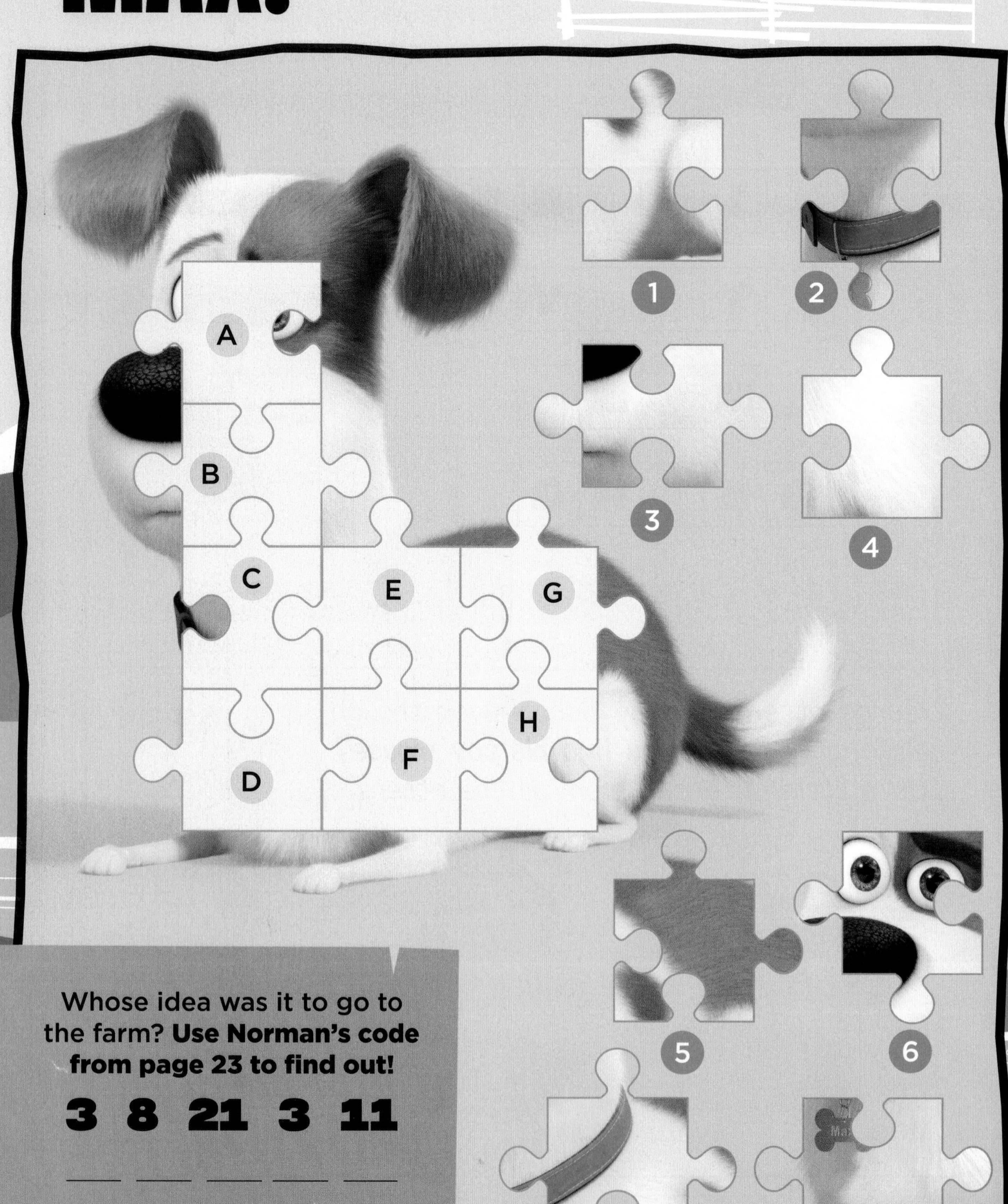

Whose idea was it to go to the farm? **Use Norman's code from page 23 to find out!**

3 8 21 3 11

____ ____ ____ ____ ____

ANSWERS ON PAGE 75

THE MISSING LAMB

Max accidentally let a little lamb escape from the farm! Max and Rooster need to find the lost lamb before something bad happens. **Help them through the maze** as fast as their paws can carry them.

FOLLOW THE FARM OBJECTS IN THIS ORDER TO FIND YOUR WAY.

What is the name of the lost lamb?
Unscramble the letters.

T O T N O C

ANSWERS ON PAGE 75

CAT COUNTDOWN

Oh no! Gidget has lost Busy Bee and she's working on a rescue plan. **Help keep track of the time** while she thinks.

WHAT TIMES DO THE CAT CLOCKS SHOW?

GIDGET IS READY AT 4 O'CLOCK.
CAN YOU DRAW THE TIME ON THE CLOCK FACE?

ANSWERS ON PAGE 75

CAT COSTUME!

To rescue Busy Bee, Gidget decides she needs a special disguise. **Complete this dot-to-dot to transform Gidget from dog to cat!**

DOODLE SOME THINGS CATS LOVE AROUND THE BRAND-NEW GIDGET.

DAISY'S READY!

FEISTY DOG DAISY HAS COME TO FIND CAPTAIN SNOWBALL! SHE'S HEARD THIS FUZZY SUPER HERO HAS WHAT IT TAKES FOR A RISKY RESCUE. COLOUR DAISY, READY FOR ACTION!

DAISY WANTS TO RESCUE HU. WHAT KIND OF ANIMAL IS HE? WRITE THE LETTERS THAT COME NEXT IN THE ALPHABET TO FIND OUT.

V G H S D   S H F D Q

___ ___ ___ ___ ___   ___ ___ ___ ___ ___

ANSWERS ON PAGE 76

LET'S SPEAK SNOWBALL!

HOW WELL DO YOU KNOW THIS COTTON-TAILED WONDER? CHECK OUT THE QUOTES BELOW AND TICK THE ONES YOU THINK SNOWBALL HAS SAID.

- IT'S SHOWTIME, BABY
- NO, NO, NO, I DON'T WANT TO GO TO THE VET
- I'M DOING SUPER HERO STUFF
- JUST CALL ME... CAPTAIN CATNIP
- SQUIRREL!!!
- I WANT TO WELCOME WHITE THUNDER BACK FROM THE WASHING MACHINE
- I RUN AND I RUN AND I RUN IN THIS WHEEL, AND I GET OUT, AND I'VE GONE NOWHERE
- HELLO CITIZENS, I'M CAPTAIN SNOWBALL

CATNAPS WITH CHLOE

Chloe was ready to lie down, but she's had a little too much catnip! **Help her unpick these puzzles** so she can get her fifth nap of the day.

1 HOW TO CAT

Gidget needs Chloe's tips on how to act like a cat. **Can you find Chloe in the picture** so she can share her cat tips?

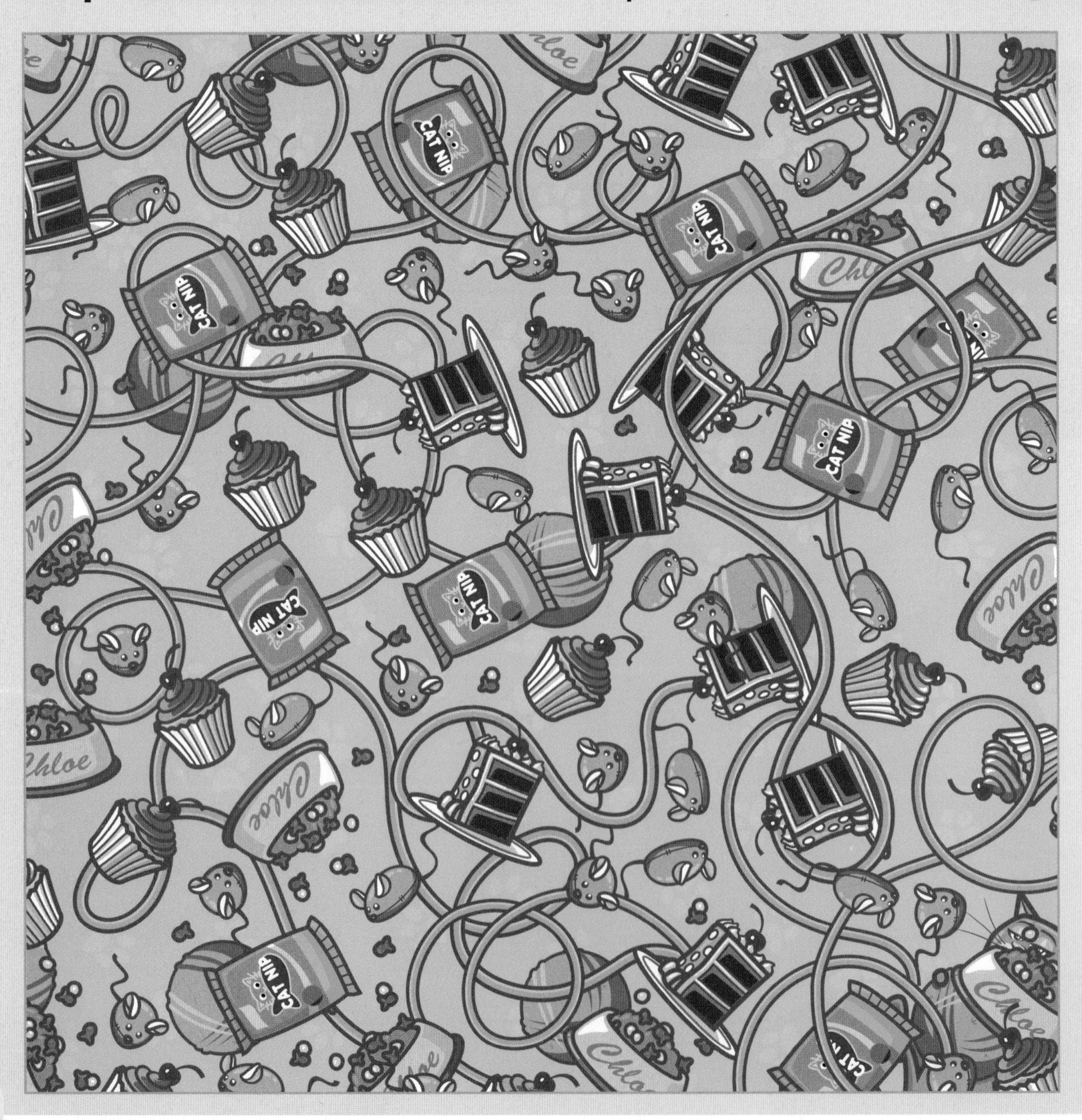

ANSWERS ON PAGE 76

2 TANGLED WOOL

Chloe is looking for her toy mouse. **Which wool line will reel him back in?**

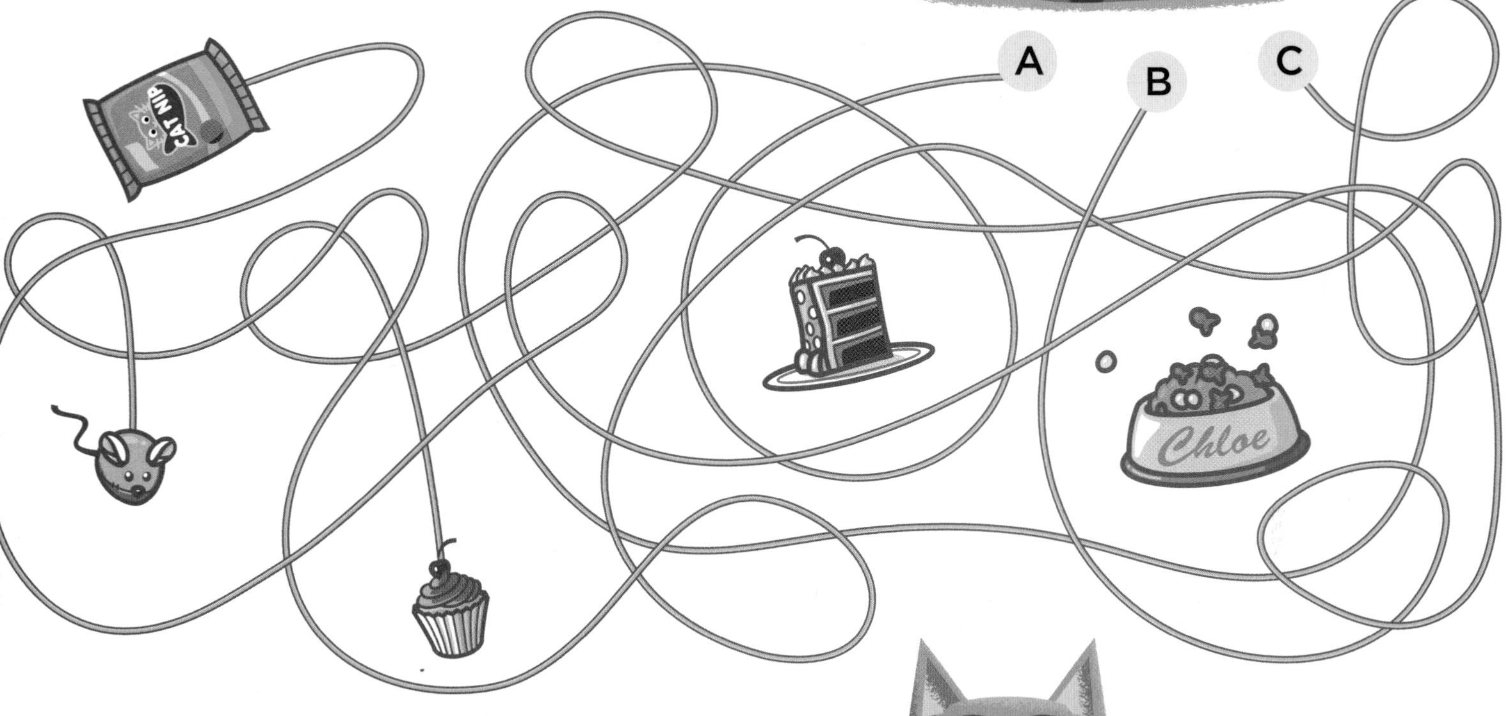

3 CURRENT MOOD

Chloe can't be bothered with all these energetic games. **Which face is an exact match for her expression?**

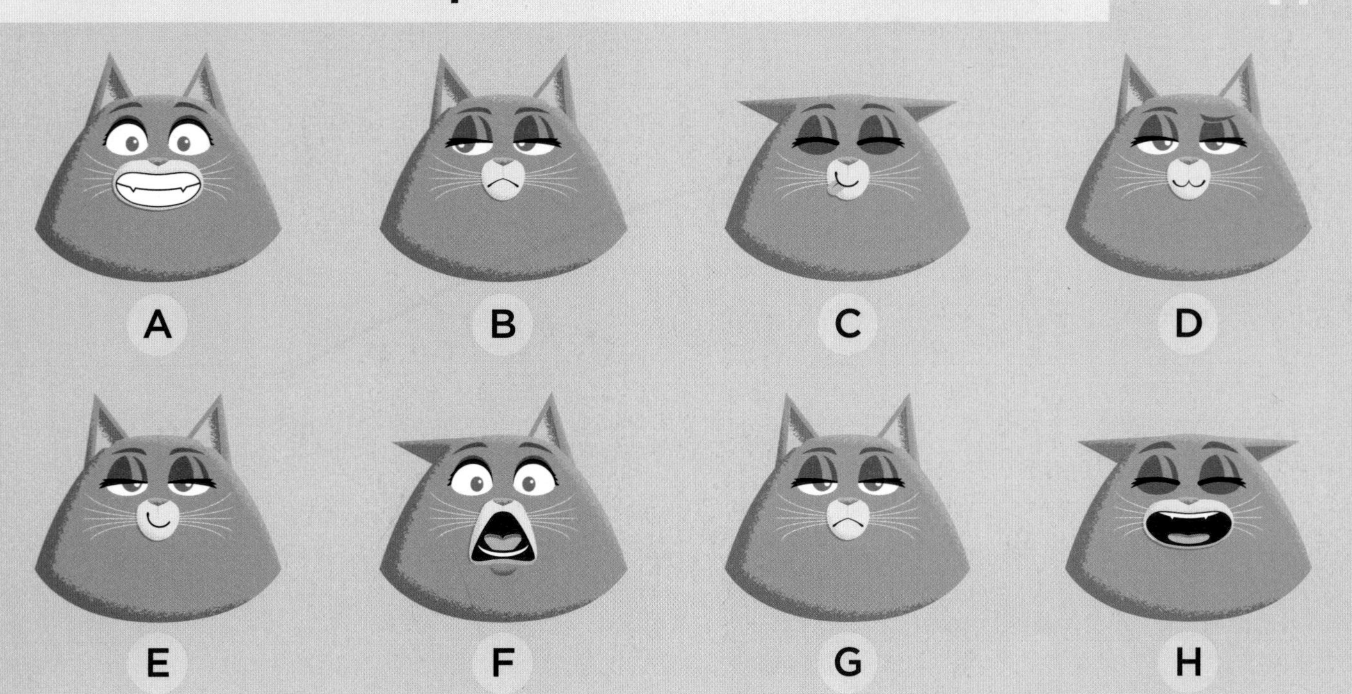

ANSWER ON PAGE 76

BUSY BEE RESCUE

This is it – Gidget is going into the cat lady's apartment to rescue Busy Bee! **Help her through the maze to pick up Busy Bee**, and **then escape to the finish**. Make sure she **avoids** the **clever cats** along the way!

START

ANSWERS ON PAGE 76

CHLOE IS HELPING GIDGET – CAN YOU SPOT HER IN THE MAZE?

FARMYARD PATTERNS

With some help from Rooster, Max is actually starting to enjoy farm life. **Can you work out which picture comes next in each line? Write the correct letter in each box.**

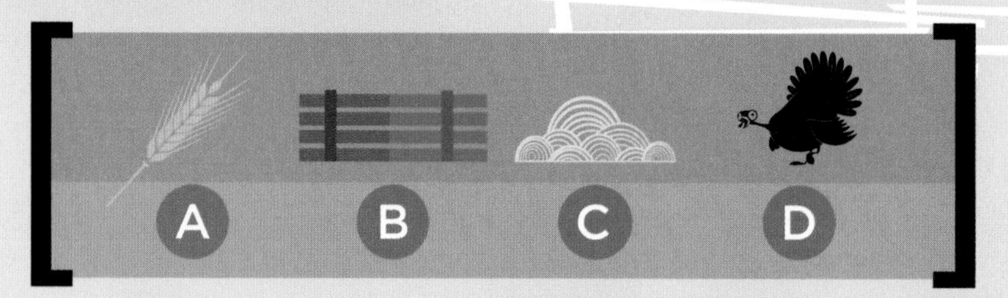

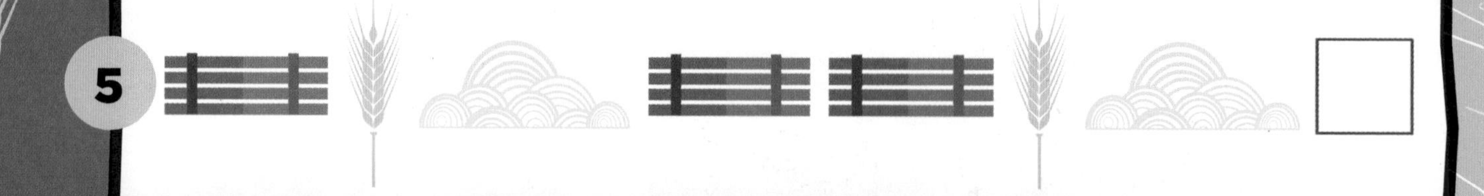

ANSWERS ON PAGE 76

DOT-TO-DOT

Max would never have survived on the farm without advice from his new friend.

JOIN THE DOTS TO REVEAL THE WISE COUNTRY DOG, ROOSTER.

Unscramble the letters to name Rooster's awesome accessory.

A N D A N B A

___ ___ ___ ___ ___ ___ ___

ANSWERS ON PAGE 76

SUPER HERO PUZZLES

THE BUCKTOOTH PET IS FINDING HIS INNER HERO. HELP SNOWBALL SUIT UP AND FACE THESE PUZZLES LIKE A CHAMP!

A WHAT IS THE NAME OF THE SUPER HERO CLOAK WORN AROUND THE NECK?

B WHO IS SNOWBALL'S NEW SHIH TZU FRIEND?

C WHICH DOG HAS A PUPPY SCHOOL IN HIS APARTMENT?

D SNOWBALL WANTS TO RESCUE HU – WHAT KIND OF ANIMAL IS HU? A WHITE

E WHAT'S THE NAME OF THE TERRIER WHO LIVES NEAR SNOWBALL?

F WHO IS THE EVIL CIRCUS OWNER WHO HAS TRAPPED HU?

G WHO IS MOLLY? SHE IS SNOWBALL'S

SNOWBALL

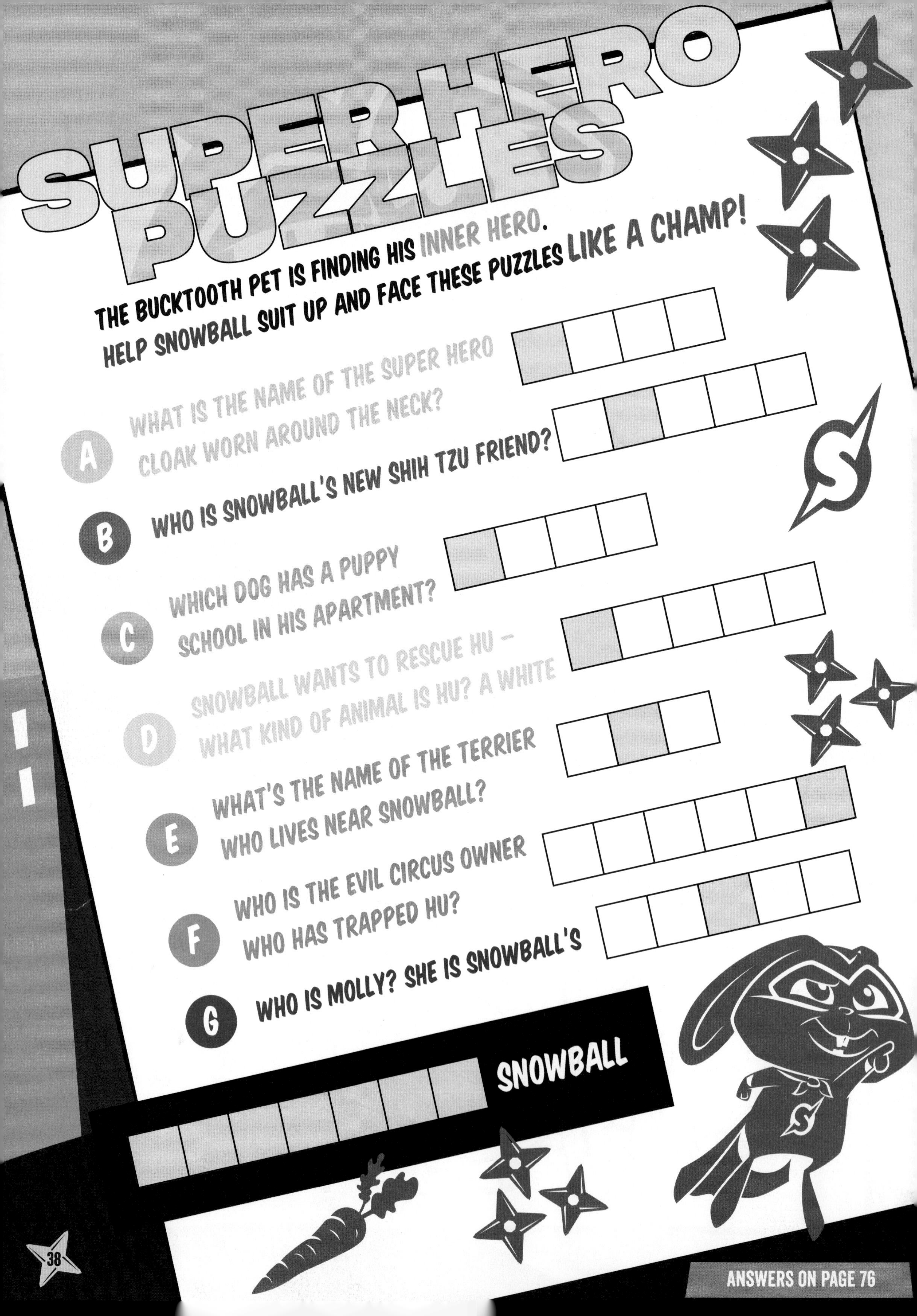

ANSWERS ON PAGE 76

THE REAL SNOWBALL

WHICH SNOWBALL IS THE REAL DEAL? FIND THE ODD SNOWBALL OUT, AND THAT'S OUR HERO.

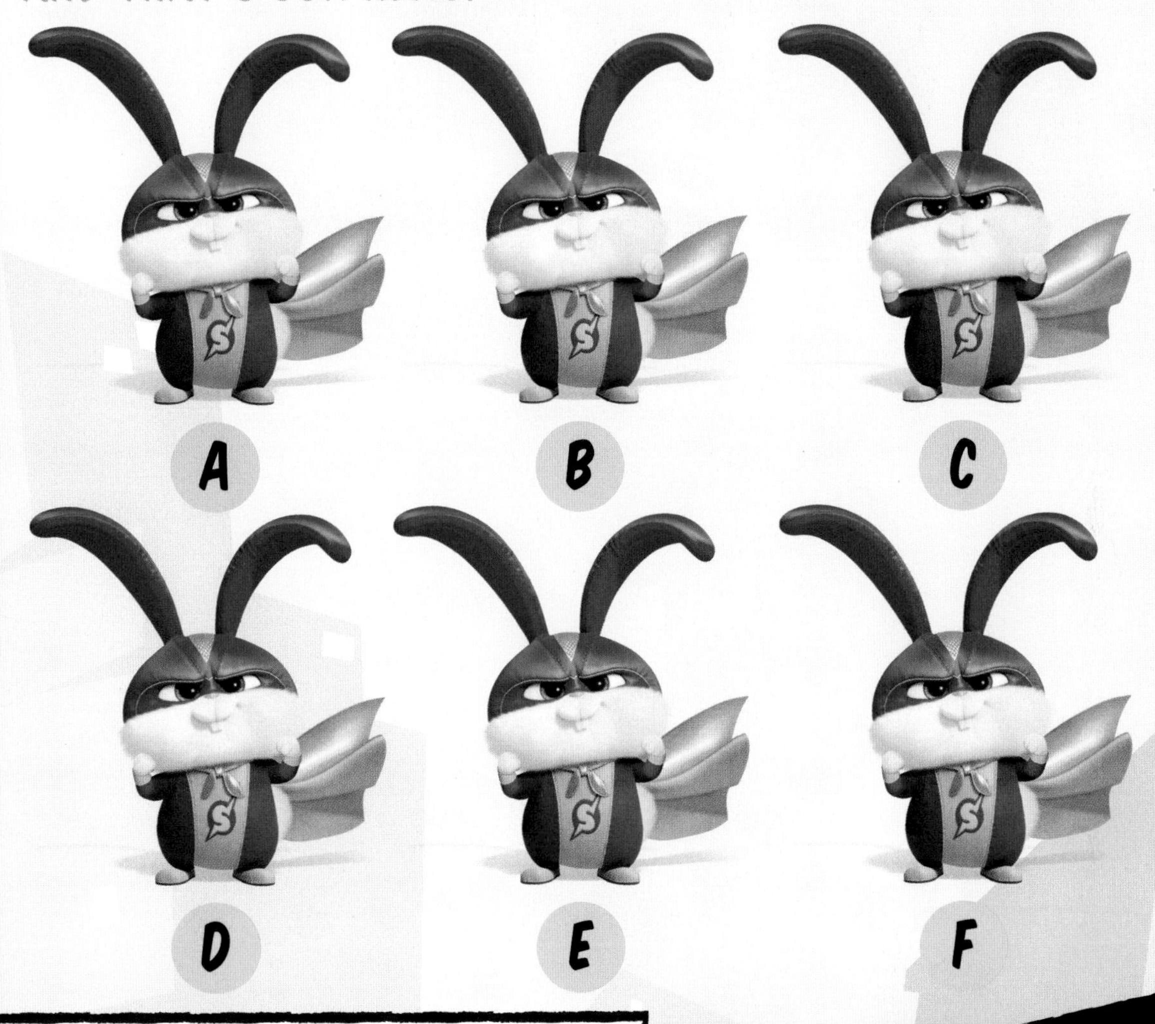

MOLLY AND SNOWBALL WERE INSPIRED BY SUPER HERO TV SHOWS. WHAT WOULD A SNOWBALL SHOW LOOK LIKE? DOODLE A SCENE ON THIS TV SCREEN.

SNOWBALL FOREVER

LIST THREE WORDS THAT YOU THINK BEST DESCRIBE SNOWBALL!

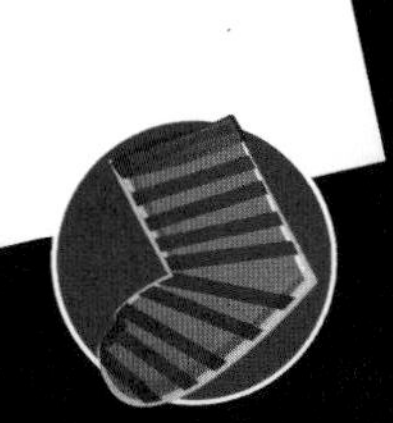

SIZE PRIZE

It's a cute-packed day at Puppy School!
Can you number the students in size order, from 1 for the smallest to 5 for the biggest?

*What **breed** of dog is the pups' teacher, Pops?*

- Basset Hound ☐
- Dachshund ☐
- Dalmatian ☐

ANSWERS ON PAGE 76

TEACHER'S PET

Which pup has perfected their puppy eyes? Find today's star student by **unscrambling the letters in the red pool balls.**

Unscramble the letters in the blue striped balls to reveal an object that Tiny has been chewing!

ANSWERS ON PAGE 76

A HOWLIN' GOOD TIME

What does a real country dog do? He climbs up on a truck and howls at the moon! **Colour** the new friends, **Rooster and Max.**

FARM SUMS

There's a lot of work to be done on the farm. **Help Rooster get these items in order by filling in the sum totals.**

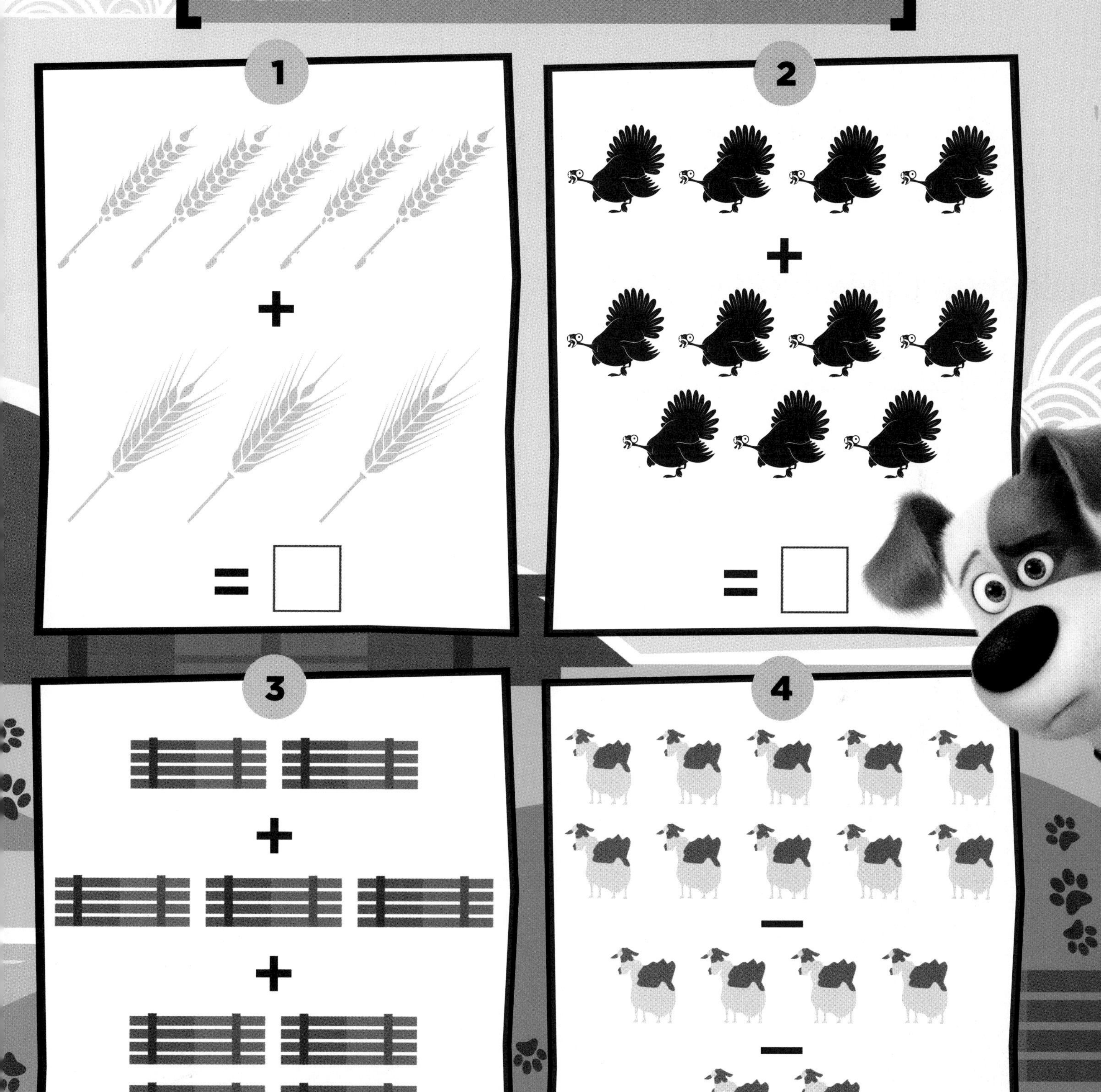

How many muddy paw prints appear on the page?

ANSWERS ON PAGE 76

A CAT'S LIFE

Gidget is strutting around in her new cat disguise. **Fill in this list with five reasons** why it would be awesome to be a cat!

1. ______________________________

2. ______________________________

3. ______________________________

4. ______________________________

5. ______________________________

WHICH GIDGET IS THE ODD ONE OUT?

1

2

3

ANSWERS ON PAGE 76

PAW MAZE

Help Gidget find her way back to her apartment by **following the cat paw prints**. How quick can you get her home?

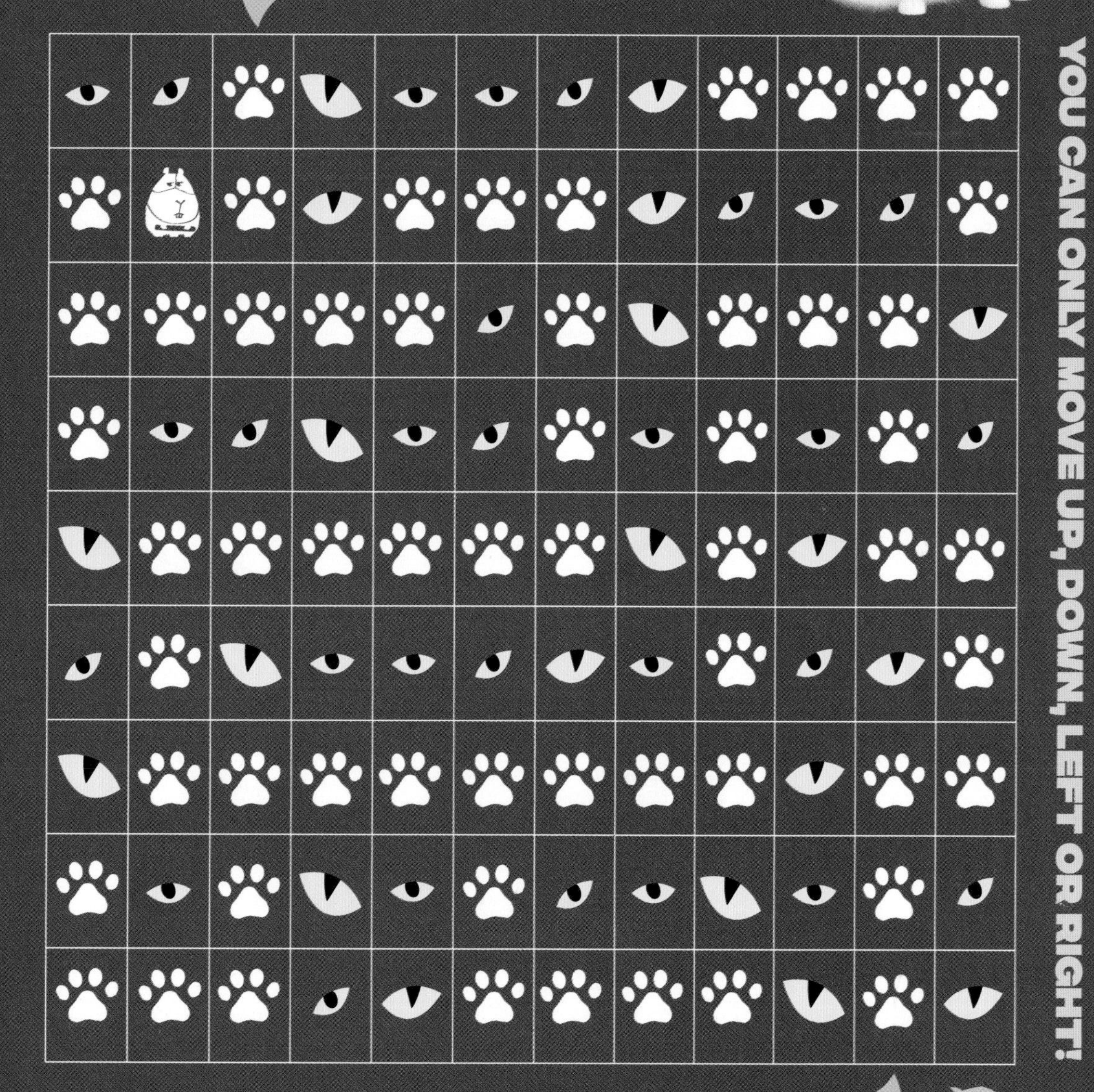

YOU CAN ONLY MOVE UP, DOWN, LEFT OR RIGHT!

CAN YOU SPOT NORMAN HIDING IN THE MAZE?

ANSWERS ON PAGE 76

DESIGN A TAG

Max is so proud of his name tag from Katie – it shows he's a proper Pet!

DESIGN A FANCY NEW NAME TAG FOR MAX.

Write Max's name on the tag and colour it in!

HOME SWEET HOME

The Pets live in an apartment building, so it's easy for them to visit each other on different floors. **In the game below, can you move down the floors from WALK to TAIL using the clues as a guide?**

HINT: Only one letter changes on each floor.

W A L K

1 A barrier made of bricks.

2 A round toy that the Pets love to play with.

3 This happens when you trip over or lose balance.

4 If you don't succeed at something.

5 A little metal object that is hit with a hammer.

T A I L

ANSWER ON PAGE 76

MAX'S CROSSWORD

Are you really, really excited for this crossword? The **clues** will have you running in circles with joy, just like Max.

ANSWERS ON PAGE 76

ACROSS

3. Worrying about baby Liam causes Max to _ _ _ _ **(4)**
5. The animal that chases Max in the farmyard **(6)**
7. A woolly animal that Max sees on the farm **(5)**

DOWN

1. The name of Max's owner **(5)**
2. The name of baby Liam's father **(5)**
4. The special toy that Max leaves in Gidget's care **(4,3)**
5. A vehicle that frightens Max on the farm **(7)**
6. The dog who helps Max learn about the country **(7)**

ROOSTER RESCUE

Uh-oh! Max has lost his way while looking for a missing lamb on the farm.

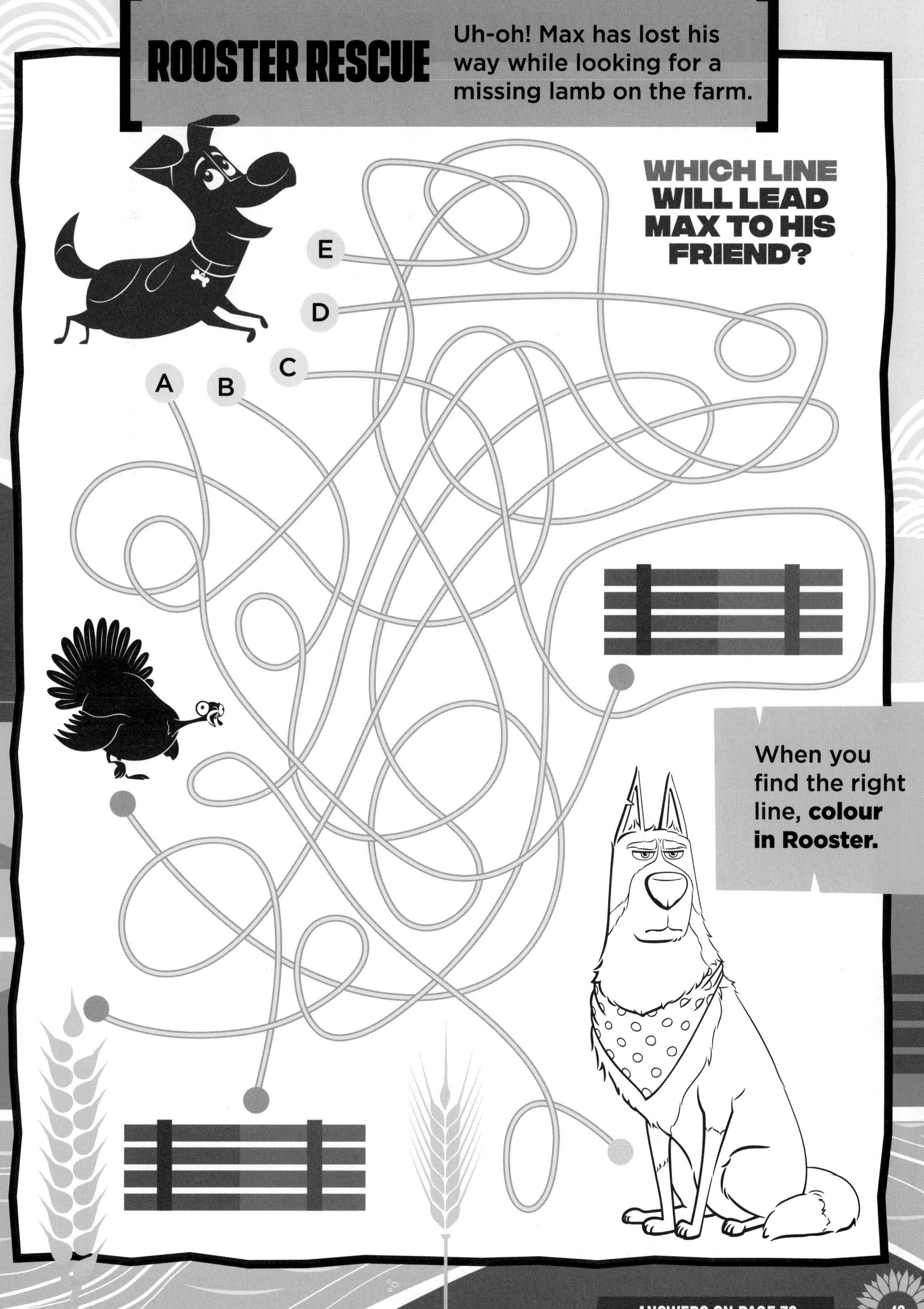

ANSWERS ON PAGE 76

LEND A PAW

Pop into the Puppy School and **help Pickles solve this word game**. Each answer begins with a letter in his name.

1. Which old dog hosts the Puppy School? P _ _ _
2. What is the opposite of outside? I _ _ _ _ _
3. What kind of animal is Chloe? C _ _
4. What is the name of Max's owner? K _ _ _ _
5. What do the pups do at School? L _ _ _ _
6. What is the opposite of difficult? E _ _ _
7. What does Snowball dress up as? S _ _ _ _ / _ _ _ _

One of the cute students has been up to mischief! **Unscramble the highlighted letters** to find out who it was.

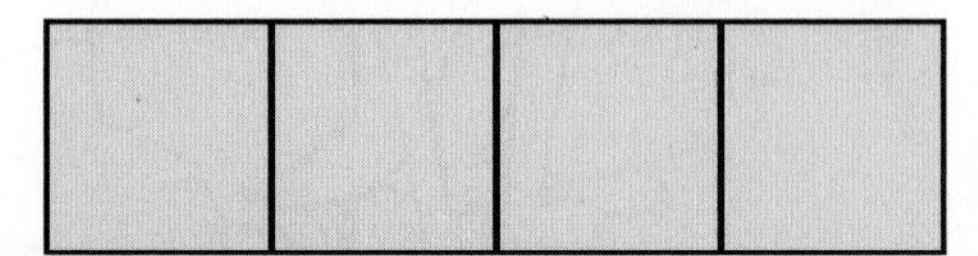

Circle the mischievous Pet!

ANSWERS ON PAGE 77

PRINCESS DIFFERENCES

Princess is catching up on her Puppy School reading.

Can you spot 6 differences in the second picture?

Colour a bone for every difference you spot.

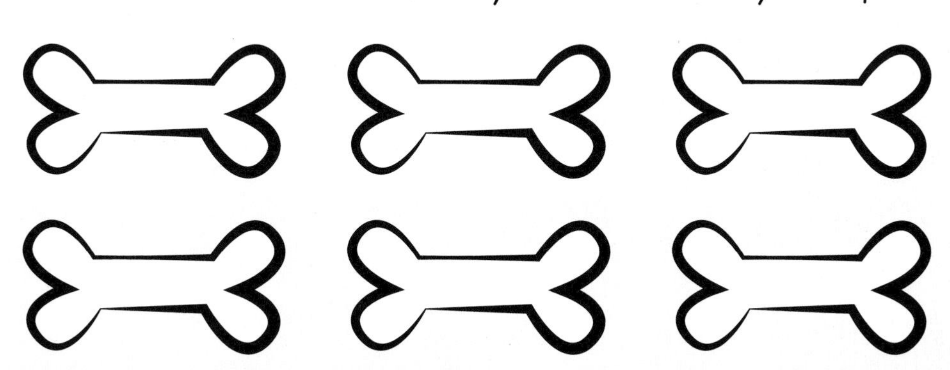

ANSWERS ON PAGE 77

PET RUMOURS

There are some strange stories floating around the Pets' apartment building. **Can you work out which are likely to be true and which are false?**

		TRUE	FALSE
1	MAX HAS A NEW BANDANA-WEARING FARM FRIEND.		
2	NORMAN IS ON A TRIP TO THE COUNTRY WITH MAX.		
3	CHLOE HAS DRESSED UP AS A DOG.		
4	SNOWBALL IS WEARING A SUPER HERO COSTUME AND PRETENDING TO FLY.		
5	A DALMATIAN CALLED PRINCESS HAS ASKED FOR SNOWBALL'S HELP.		
6	NORMAN IS USING A LASER POINTER TO DISTRACT A BUNCH OF CATS.		
7	A HUGE WHITE TIGER HAS BEEN SPOTTED IN POPS' APARTMENT.		
8	A CIRCUS OWNER CALLED SERGEI WANTS TO PLAY BALL WITH THE PETS.		
9	DAISY IS BEING CHASED BY A PACK OF CIRCUS WOLVES.		
10	MAX HAS DECIDED TO JOIN THE CIRCUS.		

ANSWERS ON PAGE 77

DUKE'S DICE GAME

Duke is a big, furry ball of fun! Take him on a city adventure and **use a dice to colour him in.**

CHOOSE AN AREA TO COLOUR, THEN ROLL YOUR DICE AND USE THE KEY TO FIND WHAT COLOUR TO USE!

COLOUR KEY

1 **Brown**

2 **Blue**

3 **Pink**

4 **Grey**

5 **Yellow**

6 **Green**

D

GIDGET JIGSAW

Let the fluff fly! Gidget's fur is all tangled up. Can you brush her back together by **putting the missing pieces in place?**

ANSWERS ON PAGE 77

SPOT THE CATS

Gidget is getting quite used to being surrounded by cats! **How many times can you spot the word CAT in the grid?**

LOOK ACROSS, UP, DOWN AND DIAGONALLY.

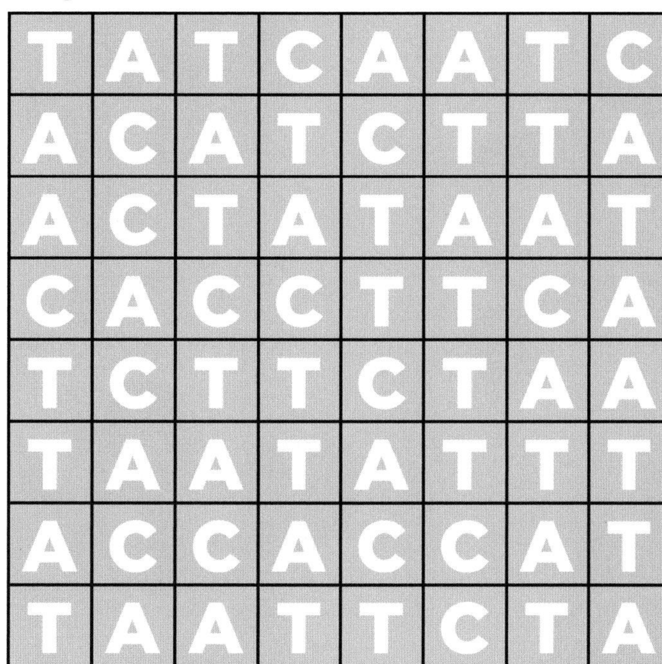

T	A	T	C	A	A	T	C
A	C	A	T	C	T	T	A
A	C	T	A	T	A	A	T
C	A	C	C	T	T	C	A
T	C	T	T	C	T	A	A
T	A	A	T	A	T	T	T
A	C	C	A	C	C	A	T
T	A	A	T	T	C	T	A

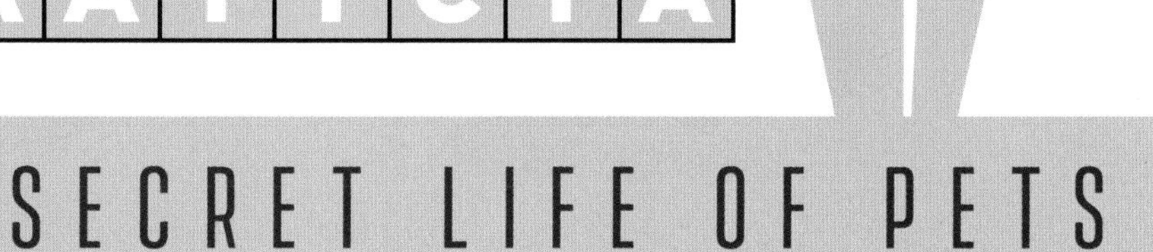

How many **new words** can you make from the letters above? For example:

POT

STEP

FLIP

ANSWERS ON PAGE 77

PUPPY MATCH

Uh-oh, the pups have been up to mischief again! Only two of the pictures of Princess, Pickles and Tiny are exactly the same. **Which two are they?**

A

B

C

D

E

F

ANSWERS ON PAGE 77

PUPS' MEMORY GAME

The puppies are playing a memory game with some of their favourite things. **Have a good look at this page and then turn over to see if you can answer the questions.**

Think back to the previous page and see if you can **answer these questions.** No peeking back!

1

Which is the correct badge for Pops' Puppy School?

A B C

2

What number was on the pool ball?

3

Which book was not in Princess' pile?

Toilet Water & Other Great Things

History of Treats

Playing Fetch for Beginners

4

How many green balls were there?

5

What colour is the toy mouse's nose?

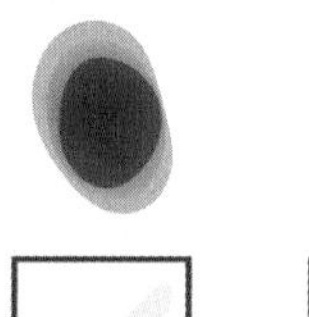

6

Which object was closest to Tiny?

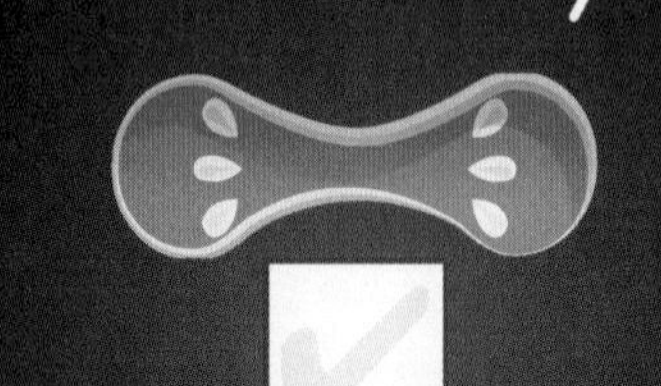

ANSWERS ON PAGE 77

WHAT'S MISSING?

The naughty pups have been hiding some items between cuteness lessons.
Can you work out what's missing in each line?

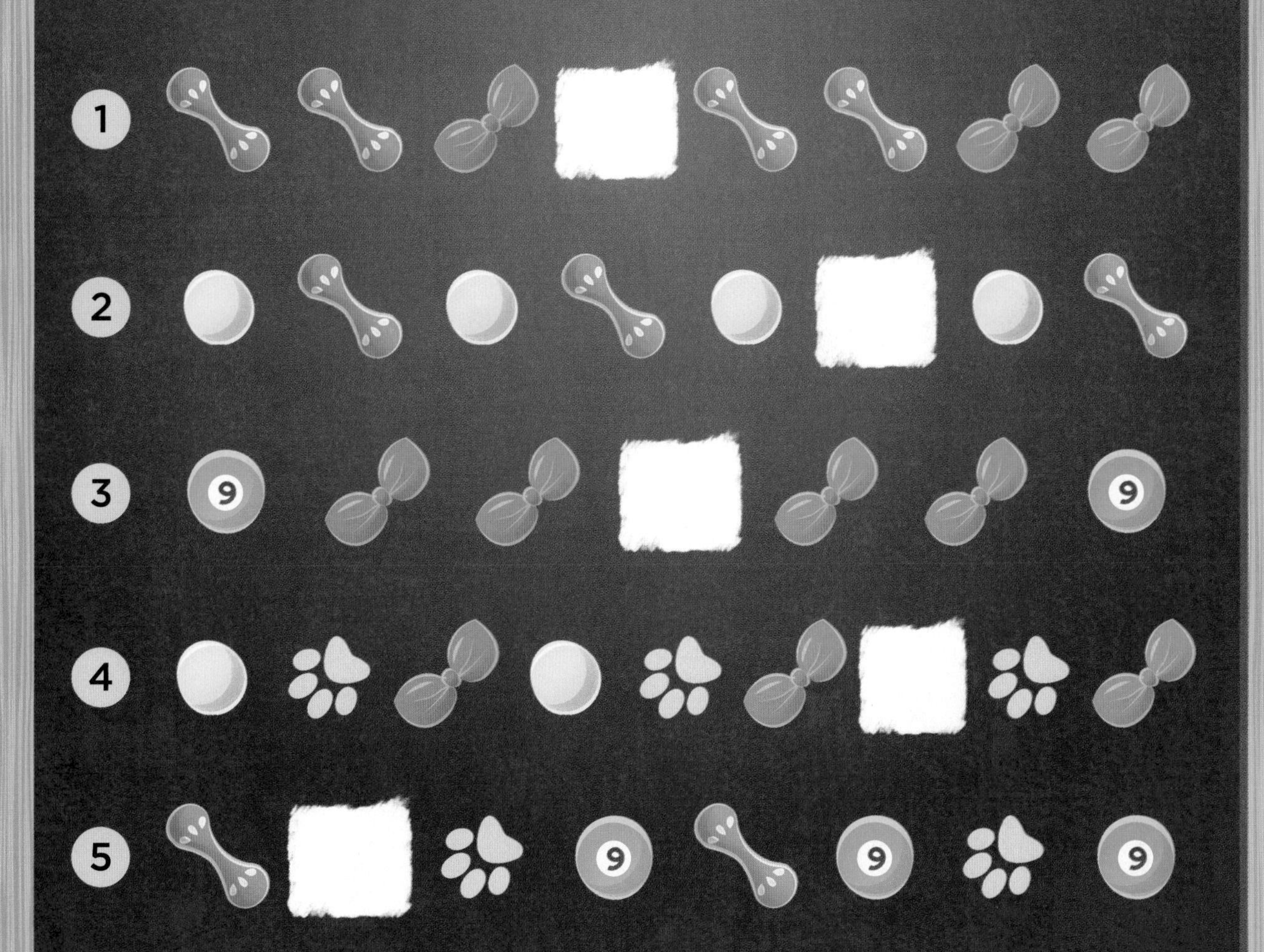

ANSWERS ON PAGE 77

SUPER SNOWBALL!

WHICH PICTURE IS A PERFECT MATCH FOR CAPTAIN SNOWBALL? FIND THE PICTURE THAT LOOKS EXACTLY LIKE HIS POSTER IMAGE!

1

2

3

4

TRACE OVER SNOWBALL'S SUPER HERO LOGO AND COLOUR IT IN.

5

6

7

ANSWERS ON PAGE 77

SNOWBALL FRAME CRAFT

TRY THIS CRAFT AND CREATE A PHOTO FRAME THAT'S FIT FOR A SUPER HERO.

USE STICKY TAPE TO ADD A SMALL LOOP OF STRING ON THE BACK OF YOUR FRAME SO YOU CAN HANG IT UP.

WHAT TO DO:

- ASK AN ADULT TO HELP YOU CUT OUT ALONG THE DOTTED LINE.
- GLUE THE PAGE TO A PIECE OF CARD (A CEREAL BOX WILL DO).
- ASK AN ADULT TO HELP YOU CUT OUT THE CENTRE AREA TO CREATE THE FRAME SHAPE.
- CUT ANOTHER PIECE OF CARD THE SAME SIZE AS THE FRAME. THIS WILL BE THE BACK OF YOUR FRAME.
- GLUE THREE EDGES OF THE FRONT AND BACK OF YOUR FRAME AND STICK THEM TOGETHER – MAKE SURE YOU LEAVE ONE SIDE OF THE FRAME UNSTUCK.
- SLIP YOUR PHOTO INTO THE SIDE THAT IS NOT GLUED.

THINGS YOU CAN DO WITH YOUR FRAME:

- INCLUDE A PICTURE OF YOUR OWN SUPER PET!
- CUT OUT A PICTURE OF YOUR FAVOURITE PET FROM THIS BOOK TO PUT INSIDE.
- WRITE A SPECIAL MESSAGE TO KEEP INSIDE THE FRAME.
- MAKE THE FRAME AS A GIFT FOR SOMEONE.
- USE THE FRAME AS A TEMPLATE TO MAKE MORE FRAMES WITH YOUR OWN DESIGN.

SNOWBALL MYSTERY WORD

IT'S TIME FOR A SNOW-STORM! CAN YOU SOLVE THE COTTON-TAILED CLUES AND WRITE THE ANSWERS IN THE GRID?

1.
2.
3.
4.
5.
6.
7.
8.
9.

1. WHAT IS THE NAME OF THE DOG WHO COMES TO SNOWBALL FOR HELP?
2. WHAT'S THE NAME OF THE ANIMAL THAT SNOWBALL RESCUES?
3. WHAT IS ANOTHER NAME FOR THE CLOAK THAT MOLLY TIES AROUND SNOWBALL'S NECK?
4. SNOWBALL HAS BUCK ______. WHAT IS THE MISSING WORD?
5. WHAT ORANGE SNACK WOULD KEEP SNOWBALL HAPPY ALL DAY?
6. WHAT COLOUR IS SNOWBALL?
7. WHAT KIND OF STRIPED ANIMAL DOES SNOWBALL TRY TO SAVE?
8. WHAT'S THE NAME OF THE CIRCUS OWNER WHO CHASES SNOWBALL?
9. WHAT'S THE NAME OF SNOWBALL'S BELOVED OWNER?

WHEN YOU FINISH, THE HIGHLIGHTED SQUARES WILL REVEAL THE MYSTERY WORDS CONNECTED TO SNOWBALL!

ANSWERS ON PAGE 77

ALL ABOUT MAX

Which four words do you think best describe Max?
Circle your choices below.

LOYAL
SNEAKY
NERVOUS
LARGE
BRAVE
FRIENDLY
SMALL
ADVENTUROUS
SHY
ANGRY
EXCITABLE
LAZY

What four words best describe you?
Write them in the spaces below.

ROOSTER'S LESSON

Max's visit to the farm is a fun trip, and he learns a lot about confidence from Rooster. Here are some ways to be more confident, just like Max.

1. STAND UP STRAIGHT AND SMILE!
2. DON'T BE AFRAID TO TRY NEW THINGS.
3. REMEMBER THAT IT'S OKAY TO NOT BE THE BEST AT SOMETHING – EVEN THE MOST TALENTED PEOPLE HAD TO START SOMEWHERE.
4. PRACTISE HARD AT THINGS YOU LIKE.
5. DON'T FOLLOW THE CROWD. CHOOSE THE THINGS THAT YOU LIKE.

Can you complete the list with five more confidence tips of your own?

6.
7.
8.
9.
10.

WOULD YOU RATHER...

Play this game with Gidget and
tick just one option for every question!

WHAT WOULD YOU RATHER DO...

BE A DOG **OR** BE A CAT?

CLEAN OUT CHLOE'S CAT LITTER

OR

TAKE MEL FOR A WALK?

VISIT THE FARM WITH MAX

OR

HANG OUT IN THE CITY WITH SNOWBALL?

HAVE NORMAN AS A PET

OR

HAVE SWEET PEA AS A PET?

CREATE A COSTUME FOR GIDGET
OR
DESIGN A COSTUME FOR SNOWBALL?
GET A HUG FROM HU
OR
PLAY IN THE MUD WITH ROOSTER?
HAVE DAISY AS A PET
OR
HAVE CHLOE AS A PET?
BE ABLE TO TALK TO ANIMALS FOR A WEEK
OR
BECOME AN ANIMAL FOR ONE DAY?

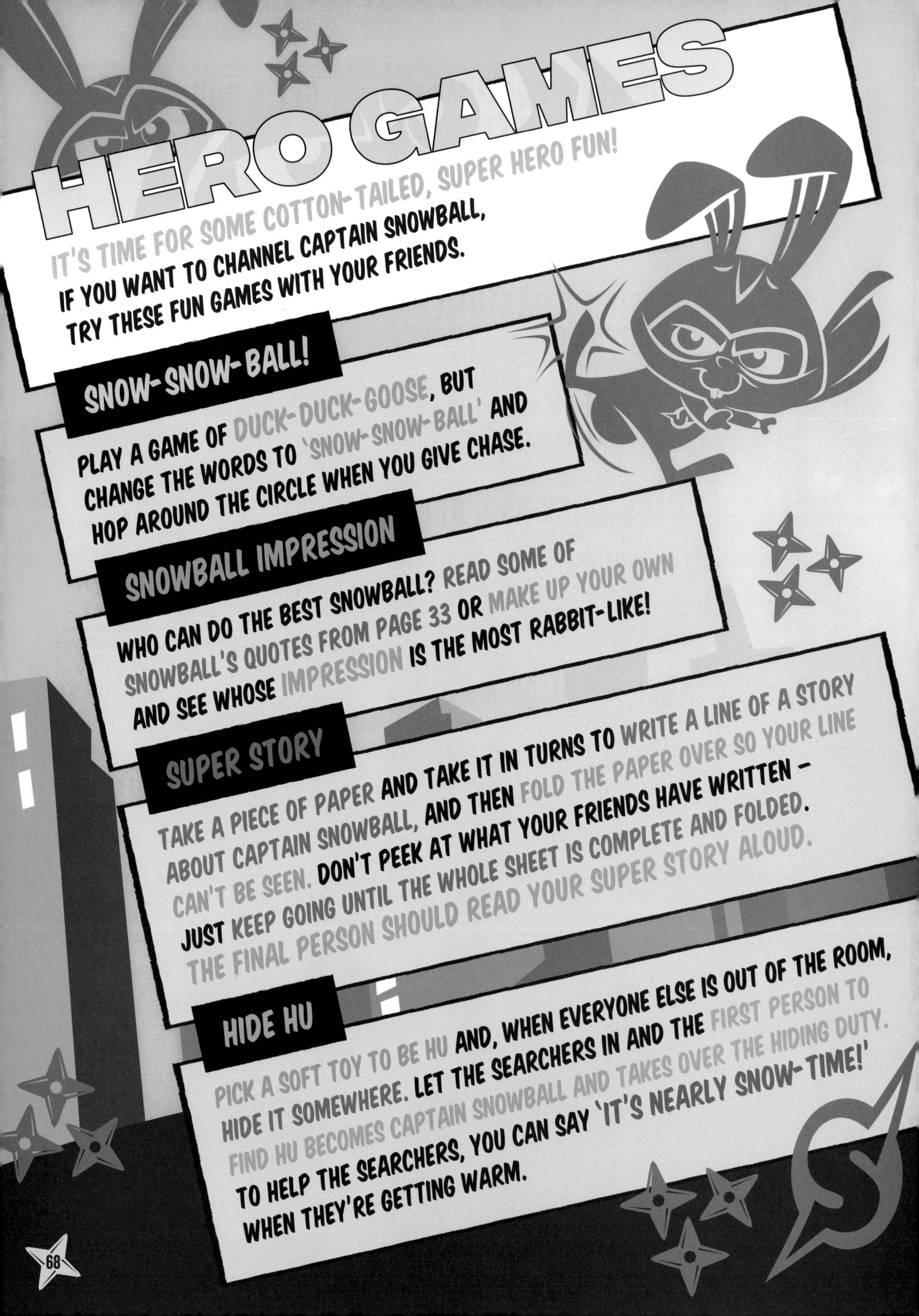

HERO GAMES

IT'S TIME FOR SOME COTTON-TAILED, SUPER HERO FUN! IF YOU WANT TO CHANNEL CAPTAIN SNOWBALL, TRY THESE FUN GAMES WITH YOUR FRIENDS.

SNOW-SNOW-BALL!

PLAY A GAME OF DUCK-DUCK-GOOSE, BUT CHANGE THE WORDS TO 'SNOW-SNOW-BALL' AND HOP AROUND THE CIRCLE WHEN YOU GIVE CHASE.

SNOWBALL IMPRESSION

WHO CAN DO THE BEST SNOWBALL? READ SOME OF SNOWBALL'S QUOTES FROM PAGE 33 OR MAKE UP YOUR OWN AND SEE WHOSE IMPRESSION IS THE MOST RABBIT-LIKE!

SUPER STORY

TAKE A PIECE OF PAPER AND TAKE IT IN TURNS TO WRITE A LINE OF A STORY ABOUT CAPTAIN SNOWBALL, AND THEN FOLD THE PAPER OVER SO YOUR LINE CAN'T BE SEEN. DON'T PEEK AT WHAT YOUR FRIENDS HAVE WRITTEN – JUST KEEP GOING UNTIL THE WHOLE SHEET IS COMPLETE AND FOLDED. THE FINAL PERSON SHOULD READ YOUR SUPER STORY ALOUD.

HIDE HU

PICK A SOFT TOY TO BE HU AND, WHEN EVERYONE ELSE IS OUT OF THE ROOM, HIDE IT SOMEWHERE. LET THE SEARCHERS IN AND THE FIRST PERSON TO FIND HU BECOMES CAPTAIN SNOWBALL AND TAKES OVER THE HIDING DUTY. TO HELP THE SEARCHERS, YOU CAN SAY 'IT'S NEARLY SNOW-TIME!' WHEN THEY'RE GETTING WARM.

CAPTAIN COLOURING

HELLO, NEW YORK CITY! CAPTAIN SNOWBALL, AT YOUR SERVICE.
COLOUR CAPTAIN SNOWBALL AS HE PREPARES FOR HIS NEXT RESCUE.

SAY CAKE!

Chloe has had her fill of fridge treats today, so she's very happy.
Complete this satisfied cat by drawing the other half of her face.

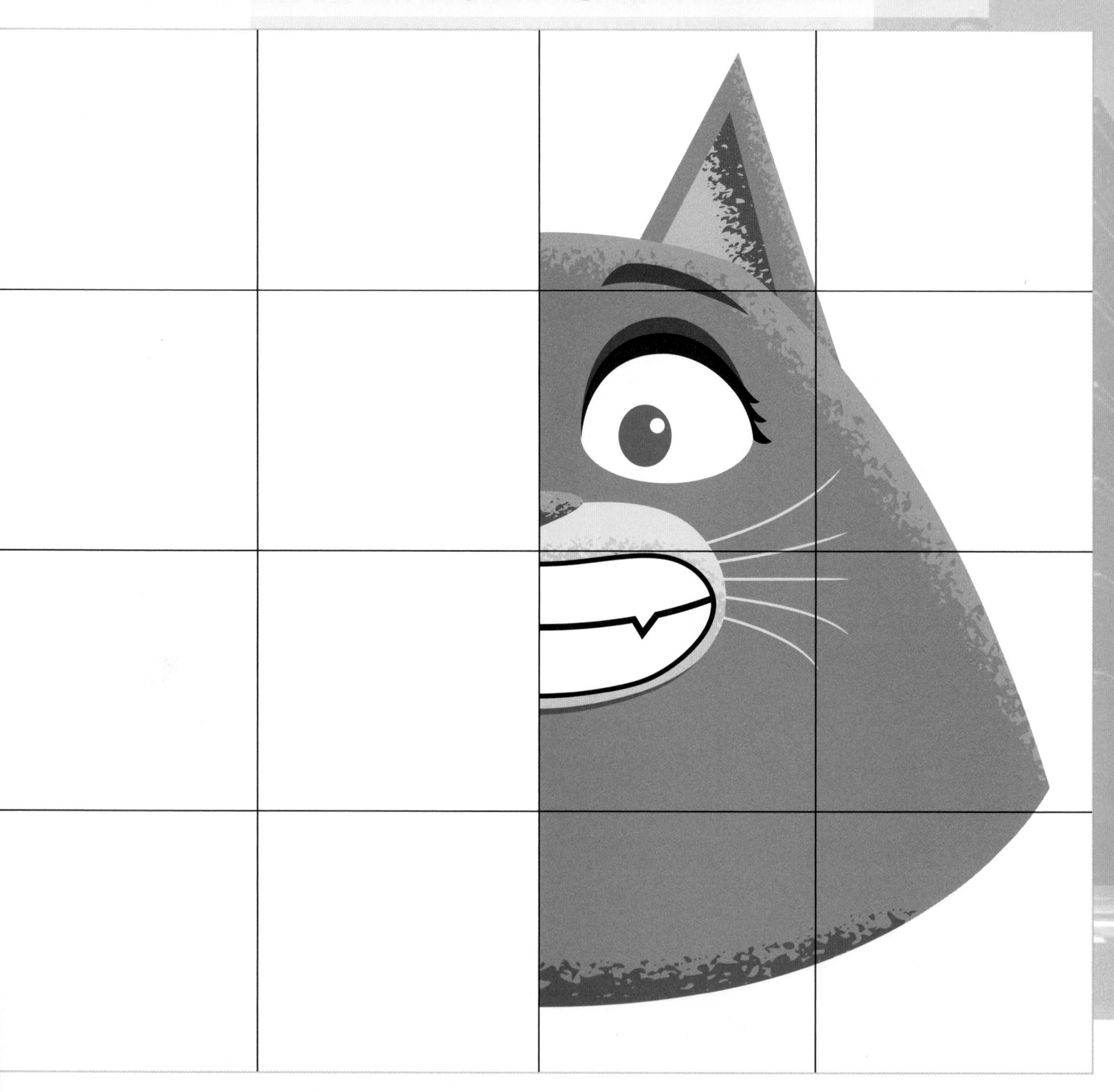

NOW COLOUR THE COMPLETED CHLOE SO YOUR DRAWING MATCHES THE OTHER HALF.

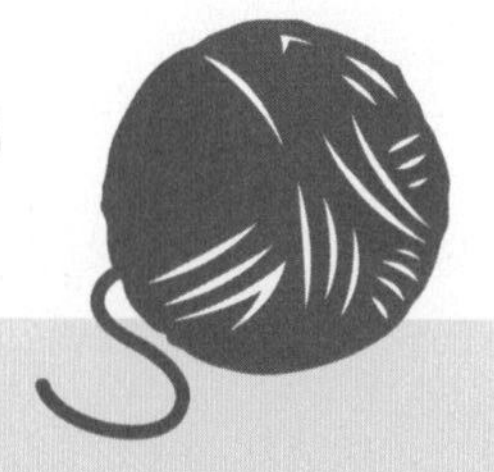

NEW YORK MAZE

Max has made it back to the city. **Help him through the maze to be reunited with his best buddies.**

START

When you find the correct path, **colour Max and his bandana.**

SECRET LIFE OF PETS 2 QUIZ!

How well do you know Max, Snowball and the rest of the gang? See how far you can get with these **trivia questions.**

EASY

TRY THESE TO GET YOUR PAWS WARMED UP!

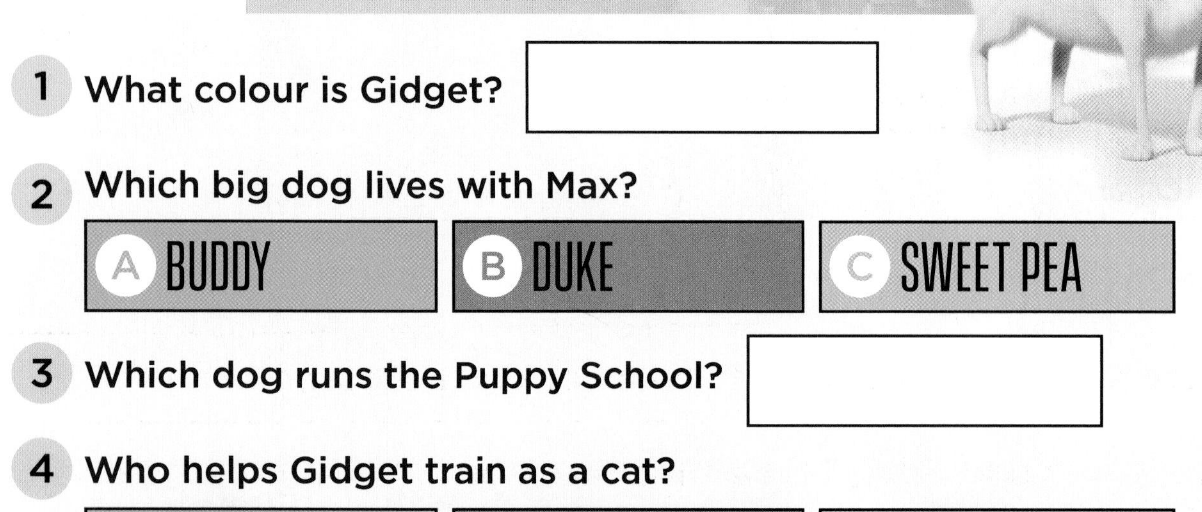

1 What colour is Gidget?

2 Which big dog lives with Max?

A BUDDY

B DUKE

C SWEET PEA

3 Which dog runs the Puppy School?

4 Who helps Gidget train as a cat?

A DAISY

B MAX

C CHLOE

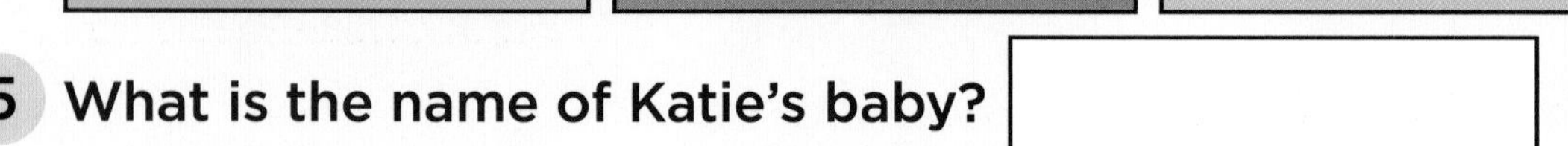

5 What is the name of Katie's baby?

6 What does Snowball like to play?

A VIDEO GAMES

B CARD GAMES

C HIDE-AND-SEEK

7 Which toy does Gidget look after for Max?

8 Which Pet is a student at the Puppy School?

A NORMAN

B PRINCESS

C CHLOE

ANSWERS ON PAGE 77

THESE QUESTIONS ARE A LITTLE TRICKIER – HOW FAR CAN YOU GET?

2 What breed of dog is Max?

3 Whose safety is Max's security team looking out for?

4 What is Hu guarded by in the zoo?

5 What animal does Gidget disguise herself as?

6 What kind of animal is Norman?

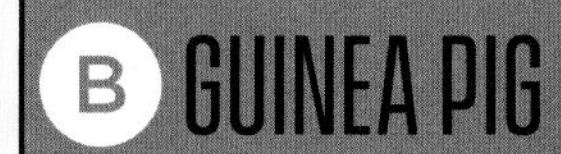

7 What animal chases Max on the farm?

8 What's the name of Max's new farm friend?

ANSWER ON PAGE 77

IF YOU CAN ANSWER THESE QUESTIONS, YOU ARE A

PETS SUPERFAN!

1 What breed of dog is Daisy?

A SHIH TZU | B TERRIER | C POODLE

2 What bedtime story does Max read to baby Liam?

A THE THREE LITTLE PIGS | B LITTLE RED RIDING HOOD | C GOLDILOCKS AND THE THREE BEARS

3 Who owns the farm that Max goes to visit?

4 What's the name of circus owner who keeps Hu locked up?

5 Who helps Gidget by using a laser pointer?

A CHLOE | B MAX | C NORMAN

6 What is Snowball's super hero name?

7 Which of these is not the name of a Puppy School Pet?

A GEORGE | B MIMI | C ARTHUR

8 What does Chloe wear on her head when she has too much catnip?

A A LAMPSHADE | B A BOWL | C A WOOLLY HAT

ANSWERS ON PAGE 77

ANSWERS

PAGE 7
The odd socks are on pages 11, 14, 18, 24, 30, 39, 41, 67, 71

PAGE 12
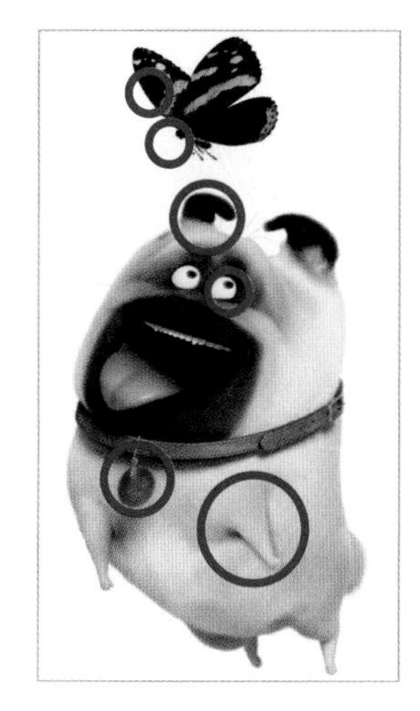

PAGE 13
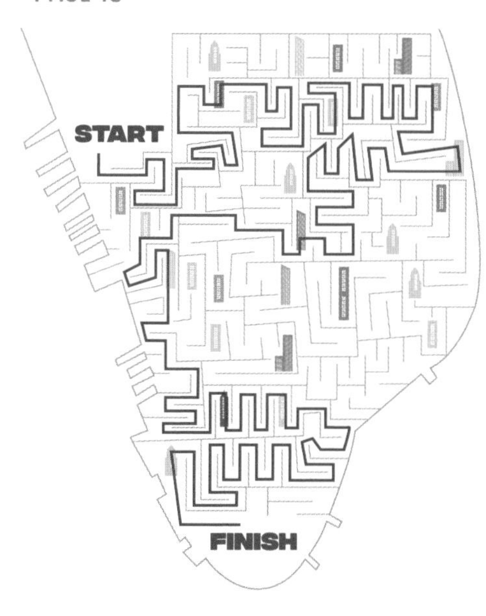

Max passes 10 buildings.

PAGES 14-15
Line C

TRACTOR COW
FENCE PIG
WHEAT LAMB

13 cows

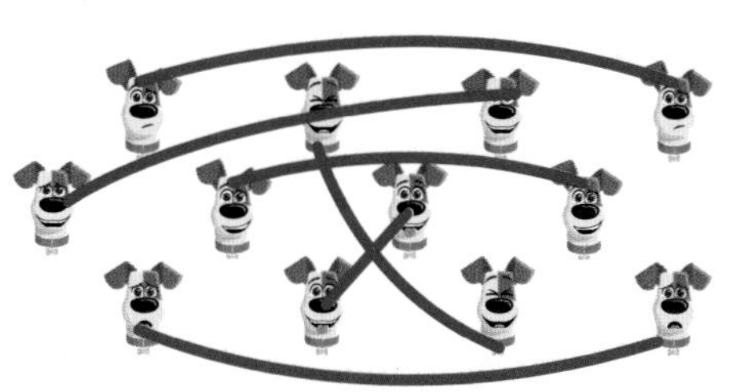

PAGES 16-17
1. 1-B, 2-C, 3-D, 4-A, 2. Busy Bee, 3. Perfume, tiara and brush

PAGES 18-19
1. 6 bows, 2. 11 paw prints,
3. Yes,
4.

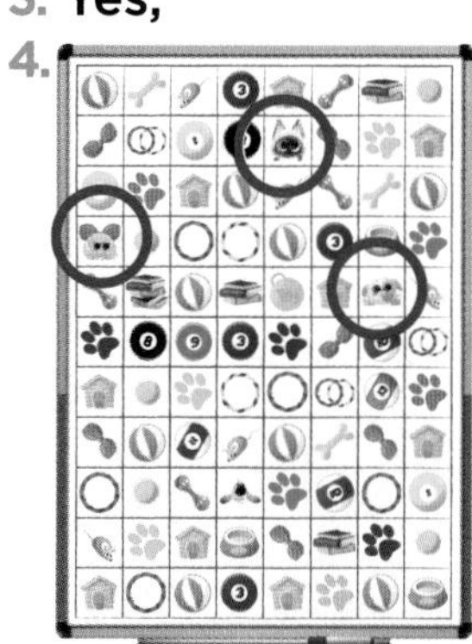

PAGE 20
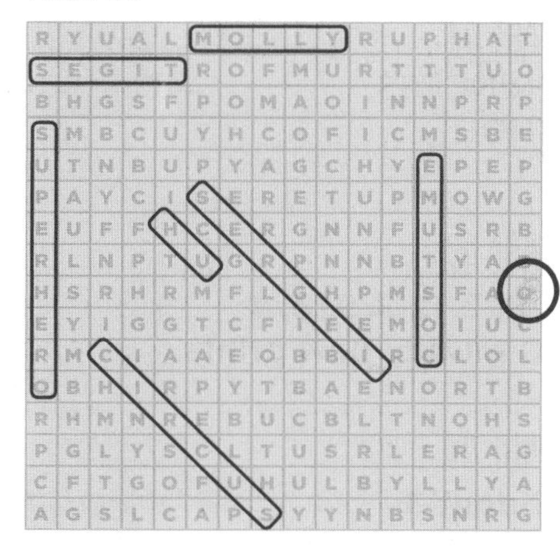

PAGE 22
GIDGET, BUDDY, SNOWBALL, MAX, DAISY, DUKE, CHLOE

PAGE 23
BABY LIAM IS MISSING!

PAGE 25
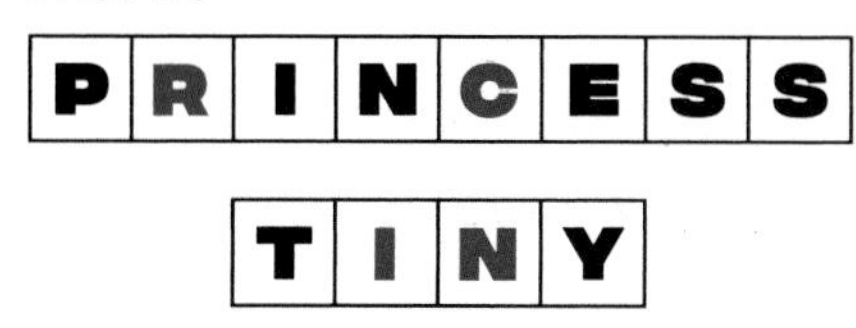

PAGE 26
1. H, 2. C, 3. B, 4. F, 5. G, 6. A, 7. E, 8. D

Chuck

PAGE 27
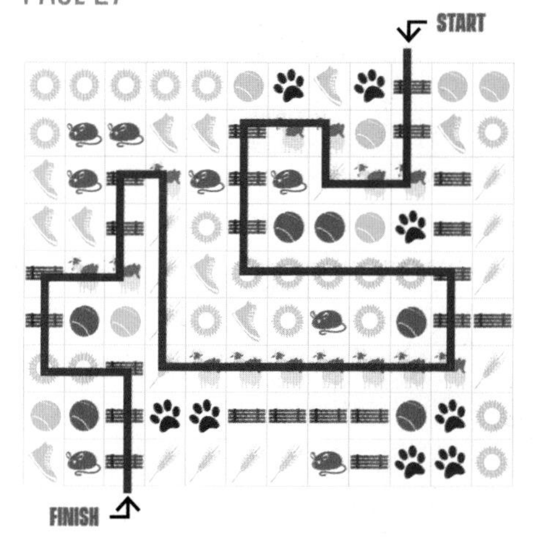

Cotton

PAGE 28
1 o'clock, 3 o'clock, 8 o'clock, half past 2, half past 10, quarter past 6

ANSWERS

PAGE 30
WHITE TIGER

PAGE 31
CORRECT QUOTES:
Hello citizens,
I'm Captain Snowball ✔

I'm doing super hero stuff ✔

I want to welcome White Thunder back from the washing machine ✔

PAGES 32-33
1.

2. C
3. G

PAGES 34-35

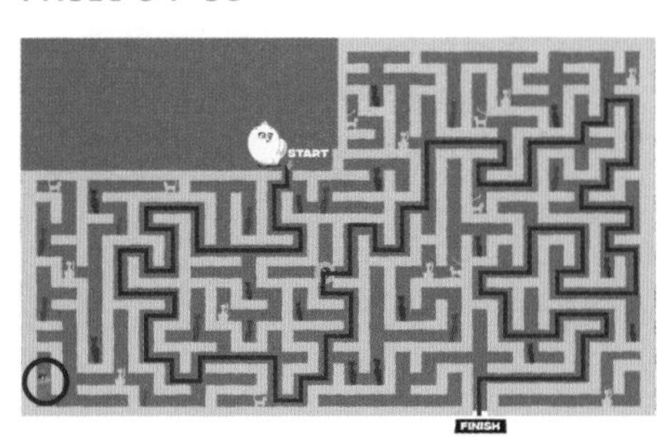

PAGE 36
1. C, 2. A, 3. D, 4. C, 5. B

PAGE 37
Bandana

PAGES 38-39
A - Cape, B - Daisy,
C - Pops, D - Tiger, E - Max,
F - Sergei, G - Owner
Captain Snowball
THE REAL SNOWBALL: D

PAGE 40

Basset Hound

PAGE 41
PRINCESS
SHOE

PAGE 43
1. 8, 2. 11, 3. 9, 4. 4
10 muddy paw prints.

PAGE 44
Gidget 3

PAGE 45

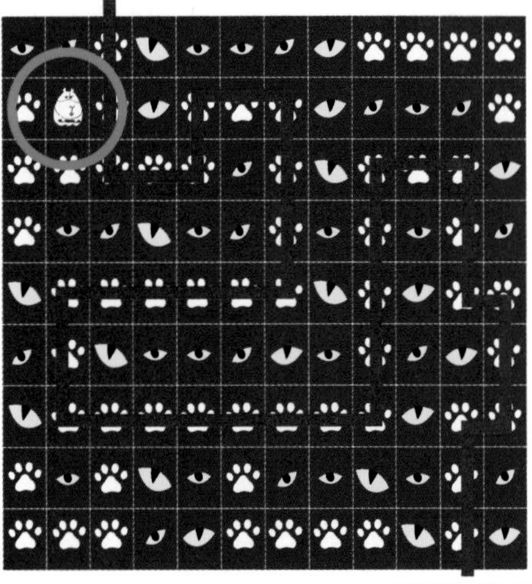

PAGE 47
1. Wall,
2. Ball,
3. Fall,
4. Fail,
5. Nail

PAGE 48

1. K						
A						
T			2. C			
3. I	T	C	H		4. B	
E			U		U	
			C		S	
5. T	U	6. R	K	E	Y	
R		O			B	
A		O			E	
C		7. S	H	E	E	P
T		T				
O		E				
R		R				

PAGE 49
D

PAGE 50

1. Pops, 2. Inside, 3. Cat, 4. Katie, 5. Learn, 6. Easy, 7. Super hero

PAGE 51

PAGE 52

1. True, 2. False, 3. False, 4. True, 5. False, 6. True, 7. True, 8. False, 9. True, 10. False

PAGE 54

1. F, 2. A, 3. E, 4. B, 5. C, 6. D

PAGE 55

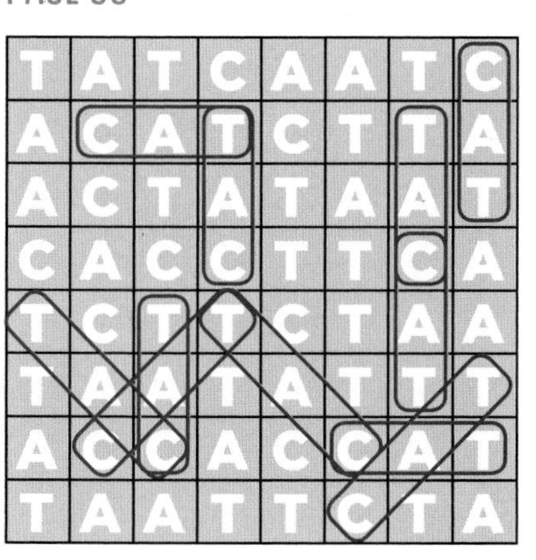

PAGE 56

C & F

PAGE 58

1. B
2. 10
3. Playing Fetch for Beginners
4. 4
5. 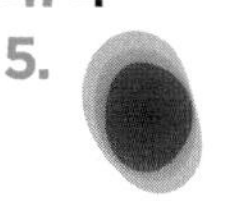
6. 

PAGE 59

1. B, 2. A, 3. D, 4. C, 5. D

PAGE 60

3

PAGE 63

1. D	A	I	S	Y		
		2. H	U			
	3. C	A	P	E		
		4. T	E	E	T	H
	5. C	A	R	R	O	T
		6. W	H	I	T	E
7. T	I	G	E	R		
	8. S	E	R	G	E	I
		9. M	O	L	L	Y

SUPER HERO

PAGE 71

PAGES 72-74

EASY: 1. White, 2. B, 3. Pops, 4. C, 5. Liam, 6. A, 7. Busy Bee, 8. B

MEDIUM: 1. C, 2. Terrier, 3. Baby Liam, 4. C, 5. Cat, 6. B, 7. Turkey, 8. A

HARD: 1. A, 2. B, 3. Uncle Shep, 4. Sergei, 5. C, 6. Captain Snowball, 7. C, 8. A